Low Carb is LEKKER®

Low Carb is LEKKER®

INÈ REYNIERSE

Photography by Sean Calitz
Styling by Brita du Plessis

Author's acknowledgements

To my husband Louis, who allowed me to feed him thin. Your passion for this lifestyle is contagious. Thanks for challenging me and being my biggest, handsomest fan, protector and provider.

To Abia, Timon, Bella and Lizzie – my lovely children. Two of you I still need to meet, but all four of you were with me during this process. You are what gives this project weight, significance and meaning. May you be bright thinkers, planet shakers and pioneers.

To my friends Herman and Helena, Francois and Suzanne, Kimmie, and Annie – you are the best! Thanks for being the best unofficial campaign team, cheering me on all along.

To Linda de Villiers, Joy Clack, Beverly Dodd, Brita du Plessis, Sean Calitz and Elizabeth Ingram, for putting my LCHF passion between the covers of a beautiful book. What an absolute honour to have worked with you. You made my recipes come to life.

To the ONE who fearfully and wonderfully made us ... I give a grateful heart.

Published in 2015 by Struik Lifestyle
(an imprint of Penguin Random House South Africa (Pty) Ltd)
Company Reg. No. 1953/000441/07
Estuaries No. 4, Century Avenue (Oxbow Crescent), Century City, 7441
P O Box 1144, Cape Town 8000, South Africa

Reprinted in 2015 (five times)

Copyright © in published edition:
Penguin Random House South Africa (Pty) Ltd 2015
Copyright © in text: Inè Reynierse 2015
Copyright © in photographs: Sean Calitz/
Penguin Random House South Africa (Pty) Ltd 2015

ISBN 978 1 43230 478 2

Publisher: Linda de Villiers
Managing editor: Cecilia Barfield
Editor and indexer: Joy Clack
Designer: Beverley Dodd
Photographer: Sean Calitz
Food styling: Brita du Plessis
Stylist's assistant: Elizabeth Ingram
Proofreader: Glynne Newlands

Reproduction by Hirt & Carter Cape (Pty) Ltd
Printed and bound by Paarlmedia, Jan van Riebeeck Avenue, Paarl, South Africa

Contents

Introduction

We have this saying in South Africa: 'local is lekker'. It simply means that local culture is something to be desired and enjoyed. We use this phrase to encourage South Africans to support their local artists, businesses, foods, feasts, produce ... you name it. It's the glue that makes us proudly South African.

After a year on a low-carb diet, I realised that my family had reached the point of no return. We felt better than ever, dropped some kilos and could think coherently ... most of the time anyway. We wanted to share the joy of our *real*, *good* nutritional values and lifestyle with others, but many people were so overwhelmed by the thought of it and figuring out recipes that I decided it was necessary to take on our proudly South African recipes and 'decarb' them!

So I started experimenting and concocting. My kitchen became a test kitchen and my camera and I became a newfound food blogger combo. A survival guide to an everyday South African LCHF (low-carb, high-fat) lifestyle had to see the light of day and mindsets had to change under less overwhelming circumstances. And I wanted to pioneer the process.

I began to envision a guide with practical know-how on low-carbing. A recipe book, a short-cut book ... a book for dummies who, like me, do not want to study nutrition but want to consume healthy, smart food and ditch disease. I read through the theories, studies and medical journals so that I could understand LCHF. I was saddened by what I discovered: so many food lies! The nutritional arena started to look like a political campaign. Who will be president: sugar or grain? It is truly worrying that people are dying from heart disease, obesity and diabetes like never before in the history of humankind!

My goal became clear. I needed to help clarify and simplify LCHF. I needed to take all those big words and turn them into layman's terms and, even better, recipes! Plain and simple. And all of this needed to happen on a budget, because low-carbing cannot be only for the rich and famous.

At this point I need to emphasise that the legacy I am hoping to leave behind with this project is that it must *never* be seen as a diet book. I don't want you to feel like this may be yet another set-up for failure. I want you to know that this is my truest effort to help you understand and feel excited about an authentic lifestyle that corresponds with our human wiring and confirms the method behind the madness through results that bring your health back into balance. It is a 100 per cent sustainable way of nutrient-dense, carb-smart 'fuelling' that could eliminate obesity and disease for good!

THE WHY, IN A NUTSHELL

So why would any person in their right mind voluntarily choose to cut back on carbohydrates, starches, grains, sugar, fructose and processed foods? I mean, everything in moderation is okay, isn't it? Is this not leaning towards the fanatical?

Many of us are allergic to wheat and gluten. Most of us will never know this because it is sold as 'healthy' food and we won't ever look in that file for the cause of illness. The wheat we eat today does not remotely have the same genetic make-up as the wheat our great-grandparents ate. Wheat and grains causes inflammation in the brain, intestines and cells. Grains and sugar cause more obesity and heart-related disasters than cream, butter and animal fat put together. Yet fats get the blame and we end up having to use more medication!

As a family we have experienced that good fats are our friends and low-fat foods actually hijack the nourishment our brains need and exchange it with harmful ingredients in the form of added sugars. You do, however, get good and bad fats, which I explain in my swap-out system (p. 20).

These are my six profound, personal reasons why you should change your eating habits:

1 My husband used to eat a 'healthy' breakfast of muesli, yoghurt and fruit. Around 10h00 he would be ravenous and eat a candy bar. Around 13h00 he would eat his 'healthy' packed lunch of

crackers or a sandwich. Around 16h00 he would feel light-headed and would struggle to focus on his work. He would come home and attack a packet of chips or a couple of bananas, cookies ... whatever he could find. He would then eat two helpings of dinner and fall asleep in front of the television, only to feel tired the next morning. What we did not realise at the time was that he was highly insulin resistant and a breath away from Type 2 diabetes. He was very overweight, and *always* tired. After changing to a low-carb lifestyle he shed 37 kg in 14 months, he has more energy than ever and no longer has cravings and sugar spikes and dips. He is now the *boertjie* (farmer's boy) who tells other *boertjies* that they will survive without their meat-AND-POTATOES regime, and the 'eat as much as you can buffet' has lost all of its carb-filled appeal. Food is not his boss anymore!

2 My son was diagnosed with autism spectrum disorder when he was only three years old. A few weeks after we had started our low-carb journey, I noticed that most of his tantrums had disappeared and more skills and integrated coping skills had emerged. Upon further research I discovered that a grain-free, low-carb, high-fat diet is the best for kids on the autism spectrum or with ADD or ADHD. It eliminates the excess inflammation of gluten in the brain and literally soothes and heals its sensitivities that can manifest in the form of awkward behaviours and emotional meltdowns.

3 My daughter is a dreamer. Some would call it ADD. We took most processed carbs, wheat and sugar out of her diet and now she is focused, slender and the pre-teen emotional roller coaster is almost half what it once was!

4 I'm a writer, voice artist, concept developer and performer and need to come up with great ideas on demand. I used to live a mostly vegetarian lifestyle – because meat and fat just did not quite do it for me – and I often found myself writing until the early hours. I became more and more forgetful and depressed. I felt old, tired and overwhelmed by life. I constantly had cravings and chocolate was my best friend. Two weeks after unhealthy carbs left

my kitchen, and I had eaten more bacon and eggs than ever, my brain came back to life, I dropped a size or two and felt like life had colour again.

5 & 6 I am expecting twins. Yes, twins! More than ever, I think cutting out inflammation-driven and insulin-spiking foods are the best gift I can give our babies. I have come to understand that prevention is better than cure and have been keeping potential food allergens out of my system from the get-go. I currently eat more than 30 g of carbs to sustain them, and also eat a slightly bigger selection of lower carb fruit. I am not striving to intentionally be in ketosis, as pregnancy is NO time for weight loss! As I am writing this book, it is still early days for me, but by the time you read this, two tiny ones might be keeping me very busy. I trust the process to be in GOOD, loving hands.

LOW CARB *IS* LEKKER

You can eat like a king! Many people have told me how they never felt like they were on a diet after changing to the LCHF way of eating, to which I always say: 'You weren't on a diet! (Diet is a four-letter word to me.) You simply embraced an anti-starving, anti-craving, stable blood sugar, eat-right regime. You connected with real-food goodness again.'

You just need to get past the initial anxiety of 'What is left to eat?', 'How will we be full?', 'This is going to break the bank!', 'What will I feed my kids?' and 'Will our livers explode?' (I get the latter a lot!)

My aim is to help you and your family find normality when you first venture into the low-carb world, from the birthday cake you bake to the dinner you enjoy with your friends. This book will teach you about swap-out foods and before you know it the mind shifts will integrate with your lifestyle as the fat melts away and your mind becomes sharper.

I am by no means a health professional. *Always* consult your doctor before changing your eating plan, especially if you have an existing medical condition or take any medication. So let's figure it out together. Sounds like a plan right?

Yours in low carb, **Inè**.

Low-carb Living – The Why

South Africa has the third-highest obesity rate in the world, with the United States of America (USA) firmly in first place and Britain second.

Almost half of South Africans are overweight to obese according to a 2014 study conducted by the Medical Research Council. Seven out of 10 women and four out of 10 men are overweight or obese, with a predominance among black women and white men over 35 years of age. Our children rank the fifth highest on the world obesity scale, with almost 17 per cent of children under nine being obese. What a cruel wake-up call!

Preventable 'lifestyle' diseases such as type 2 diabetes, certain cancers, heart disease and strokes are directly related to obesity and are among the top 10 causes of death in South Africa.

Experts are only now starting to see the true identity of the deadly culprit, and among those brave enough to expose this identity, the term *refined carbs* has surfaced time and again.

Statistics have shown that we have become really, really fat in the last 40 years. And no amount of global intervention within the last 20–40 years has made ANY difference! Not a single tub of low-fat anything, no revolutionary diet, no piece of gym equipment and certainly no pill. WHY?

To understand the roots and earliest signs of this problem, we need to take a look at England in the early 1800s and then hop over to the USA in the 1950s.

THE HISTORY OF SUGAR

Sugar has been around for thousands of years and, like most spices centuries ago, it used to be a very expensive commodity. Roman emperors would stir a teaspoon of sugar into water and use it as a remedy for tummy ailments.

In tropical areas where sugar cane grew naturally, people would mostly chew on the fibrous plant. The Chinese, however, processed the sweet syrup from the sugar cane into crystals the size of fine gravel.

As the oceans' trade routes opened up to new world destinations, sugar was introduced to Europe and America, where this sweet wonder did not occur naturally. As tropical islands in the Caribbean were colonised, it started what was called the 'sugar rush', with Britain building an enormous new empire with their 'white gold' or sugar trade. Sugar became the sweetener of choice for elite society in Britain in the 1700s, when it cost the equivalent of $100 per pound in today's money!

After improved production methods and large-scale cultivation of sugar cane in the colonies, sugar flooded the market. And then it was combined with industrially processed wheat flour and it opened up new ways of cooking. By the 1800s tea was sweetened with sugar, and recipes for jam, sweet pies, cakes, sweet breads, biscuits and chocolate were born. Although expensive, people had to have it. They had tasted life with sugar, and they loved it!

The British liked it so much that they colonised a few more islands in the West Indies and imported slaves to work in their sugar plantations. Within a few years the production of sugar was subsidised to the point where it was no longer only available to the rich, and other classes started to experience the sweetness.

At the start of the nineteenth century, the working class ate a diet of mostly bread, potatoes, cheese, butter and the occasional bacon fat. By the end of the century they were eating mostly bread, margarine, jam and cake. The average Brit consumed about 5 kg of sugar per year in the early 1800s, but that amount literally spiked to 21 kg per year by the end of the century. (Today we average about 60 kg of sugar per person per year!)

The Low-carb Hall of Fame

WILLIAM BANTING

This well-connected funeral director with strong ties to the royal families of the day – he handled the high-profile funerals of King George III and King George V – was also an extremely obese, upper class sugar lover who ended up as a self-proclaimed yo-yo dieter.

Aware of his romance with sugar and seeing the same fattening trend building up on people around him, William Banting decided to take charge at age 67. The diet was suggested to Banting by diabetes specialist Dr William Harvey, who studied under French diabetes researcher Claude Bernard in the mid-1800s, but it was Banting who self-published the first formal, modern version of a low-carb concept.

JOHN YUDKIN

This is the guy who warned us about sugar over 40 years ago!

John Yudkin was the founder of the nutrition department at the University of London's Queen Elizabeth College in 1953 (the first degree in nutrition at any European university). He was just in time to join the heated debate and frantic scientific research efforts of nutritionists across Europe and America, after heart disease levels started to reach alarming heights. For decades butter and animal fats were used without it spurring on such levels of heart disease. Yudkin immediately knew that sugar had to play a role because the British were consuming sugar at levels far higher than at any time before 1850.

Although ridiculed by the American scientist Ancel Keys, who believed that fat was the leading cause of heart disease, Yudkin released the book *Pure, White and Deadly* in 1972.

He wrote in plain English about the direct correlation between sugar consumption and the rise in heart disease. He fed rodents, chickens, rabbits, pigs and even students sugar and carbohydrates, and found raised blood levels of triglycerides, or fat, which was then, as now, considered a risk factor for heart disease. Sugar also raised insulin levels, linking it directly to type 2 diabetes. He also noted that most animals also over-ate on a sugar- and carbohydrate-rich diet, so obesity was also connected to sugar and refined carbs!

'If only a small fraction of what we know about the effects of sugar were to be revealed in relation to any other material used as a food additive, that material would promptly be banned.' – John Yudkin

The food industry launched campaigns against Yudkin, scientists condemned his work and those who agreed with him were too scared to say so in public. Yudkin became a pariah and his views were shunned. His book didn't sell and even though he stood by his scientific finds and convictions, he was publically humiliated and his career mostly ended in shame.

In recent years, Yudkin's work has been brought back into the limelight by childhood obesity specialist, Dr Robert Lustig. But this time it is being embraced by a growing, new generation of medical professionals hungry for science to meet the truth.

GET BIG OR GET OUT!
THE BIRTH OF A PANDEMIC

Let's switch on our psychedelic disco lights and time travel over to the USA in the early 1970s. In short, Nixon was president and the country was in shambles due to the war in Vietnam. Food prices were at an all-time high. Nixon, who needed to win the people's trust, appointed Earl Butz as new secretary of agriculture. Butz urged farmers to farm from fence to fence. Small-scale farming disappeared and, almost overnight, giant industrial-scale farming was born.

Bigger farms and soon bigger people followed. More produce meant more food, and that food had to be given places to go and consumers to consume it. But people didn't just want to eat a bigger plate of corn, so the Japanese came to the rescue by producing high fructose corn syrup from regular corn. Also known as glucose-fructose, this syrup undergoes enzymatic processing in order to change some of the glucose into fructose to achieve the required level of sweetness. And the syrup ends up tasting sweeter than sugar at a third of the price. With the mass production of high fructose corn syrup you could drink the corn, bake cakes and bread with corn, make medicine with corn.

What's so bad about this? Increasingly, scientists are making a connection between fructose and the way it assists in suppressing the hormone leptin. Leptin's primary function is to tell your body when you are full.

Dr Robert Lustig on fructose: 'It makes the brain think you are starving. Now what you have is a vicious cycle of consumption, disease and addiction, which explains what is happening the world over.'

The invention of the household freezer proved to be just what was missing to complete the food surplus and convenience of ready-made foods. Freezing products that were now sweetened with corn syrup gave the consumer the opportunity to store foods that were not in season. People could also buy frozen meals and sweet treats and have them anytime.

The concept of 'snacking' started in Britain and quickly found its way into other Western countries. Chocolate bars and other sweetened, processed foods were advertised as the perfect snack between meals, and soon the food business was thriving from our newly adopted snacking habits.

Then, along with the already growing fast-food chains that readily supplied bigger portions, people experienced the power of choice to supersize. Now you could drink a soda that contained up to 50 teaspoons of sugar in one sitting!

In the 1970s and 1980s, however, obesity was not a concern. Their battle was about understanding the causes of heart disease and whether fat or sugar was the culprit. Scientist Ancel Keys drove this campaign and won in favour of fat as being the main role player in heart disease. Interestingly, he did not have full support among his scientific colleagues, but he did catch the USA government's attention. And at a time when corn syrup production was booming, the government supported Ancel's very weak theory that saturated fat intake had probable links to clogging the arteries and causing heart disease.

The plot really 'sickens' from this point on, but THIS marked the point when most people were told by the food industry that they needed to eat less saturated fat and more plant fats such as margarine, and that if they loved their hearts, they should eat low-fat foods, which the food industry supplied in abundance. And when the taste was compromised by taking out the fat, they compensated with ... you guessed it ... sugar!

'You really have this huge load of sugar going to the liver and that's the impact. Not only on the fats in the blood that may lead to cardiovascular disease, but also maybe to fat accumulation in the liver which could have some impact on diabetes and some other chronic diseases.' – Dr Jean Marc Schwarz, Touro University, California

By 1993 obesity rates soared. Pharmaceutical companies made millions out of diet pills and diet books were everywhere. Almost everyone was aware of calorie intake or was on a new weight-loss programme.

After 40 years of low-fat living, why are we more obese than ever? Our arteries are still clogged, we die of more types of cancers, active young people suffer from diabetes and more people die without the dignity of recognising their loved ones due to Alzheimer's. Autism numbers are spiking along with other brain-based illnesses.

'Genetically we have not changed, but our environment and access to cheap food has changed.' – Professor Jimmy Bell, British Medical Research Council
[Special credit to the informative 2012 BBC Two documentary *The men who made us fat*.]

An LCHF lifestyle is all about eating *real* food, food that cannot keep fresh for too long, for a reason... It's what we were created to eat all along!

ANCIENT MENUS

So what exactly did some ancient civilisations eat? Why do we limit noble things such as bread and fruit on a low-carb diet? I've researched the foods of the ancient Egyptians and Israelites and in very broad and shortened terms, they ate:

Meat

They ate mostly two meals a day, one mid-morning and the other in the evening, usually in the form of meaty stews or soups. The meat was usually goat or lamb (beef was for royalty) and they also ate wild poultry, chicken and a lot of fish. The sheep's tail was a fatty cut and seen as an absolute treat.

Fruit, nuts and seeds

During the summer months they ate a variety of about six fruits at the most, usually dates, figs (also wild sycamore figs), mulberries, melons, apricots and grapes. Some regions had apples. The rest of the year they would occasionally have small quanti-ties of dried fruit pressed into a mould called a fruit cake. Fruits such as figs and dates were boiled into a syrup and this was called honey. This date honey was precious and used as a sweetener or to flavour certain dishes. Grapes were preserved in the form

of wine and were only eaten fresh after a harvest. Only royalty could afford coconuts.

They ate various nuts and seeds on a seasonal basis, and made oil from seeds and olives. This was part of the daily diet. Honey from bees was found in the wild and seen as a delicacy. It was the food of royalty and not something to be devoured daily.

Veggies

The poor dug in the fields for wild tubers that were small and very fibrous. Otherwise they ate what they produced in their veggie patch in season, such as leeks, garlic, onions, herbs and squash. Mushrooms were gathered after the rain.

Grains and legumes

They ate chickpeas and lentils in stews when meat was not available or was scarce.

To bake a bread for a family of five would have taken three hours of hard labour before it even went into the clay oven. This was a daily exercise. Imagine grinding for hours and then watching your family eat a hand-size piece of flat bread in minutes!

The wheat available at that time was very hard to grind and was pressed into a flat loaf, which was broken into pieces before eating. Not at ALL like the fluffy breads we know today. Their use of primitive equipment meant that a lot of the husks remained, so the bread contained fibre galore! The gluten content of these grains was also much lower.

Dairy

Food was regularly fried or cooked in homemade butter, and they made cheese and cultured (soured) milk and yoghurt.

TODAY'S MENU

We live in a modern society where in one 5-minute trip to the store you can buy food from all continents and all four seasons at the same time. You can buy food that has grown without ever seeing the sun, food that was developed in a laboratory, food that was made to mimic the real thing ... all under the banner of convenience.

Gary Taubes, the award-winning American science writer, says we are not fat because we eat too much, but we eat too much because we are fat. The fatter we get, the more our fat cells need to be fed.

We have moved away from one of the most basic principles of sustained life: food is supposed to be eaten to fuel and maintain our bodies. Instead, food has become a form of comfort, our happy place or a pick-me-up. We even reward our children's good behaviour with something sweet.

Don't get me wrong, I'm the first person to tell you that we need to celebrate life, and what better way is there to do it than with a feast of beautiful food? But my plea is that you be fuel smart! LCHF gives an authentic guide to times when food was used to fuel and sustain within season and availability. Summer is meant to provide you with abundance and if you are fortunate enough, you should have some fat reserves for winter.

Let's not fuel with glucose, sucrose, high fructose corn syrups, modified hydrogenated oils etc. Eat fruit by all means, but understand that a bowl of three or more kinds of fruit used to be a dessert for kings during a festival, not everyday fare!

We are, however, South Africans living in a modern society. That is why I 'decarb' the foods we know and love and use nuts and seeds to bake instead of wheat flour. It is easier to adapt to an LCHF lifestyle if the dishes you eat are familiar, even if some of the ingredients may not be!

Is all wheat bad for us?

Yes, it is! And here's why:

1 Wheat triggers cravings for more carbohydrates. The gliadin protein in wheat drives the appetite, causing us to want to eat more. People who allow wheat into their diet tend to overeat by 1 600 kJ per day.

2 Fat from wheat usually accumulates around the belly, where it causes inflammation. This triggers an emergency inflammation signal in the bloodstream, which in return raises blood sugar, blood pressure and triglycerides.

3 Wheat is single-handedly responsible for a much higher LDL (bad cholesterol) density in individuals and is directly linked to heart disease. Ironically, we have been told to cut the fat and do 'healthy' whole grains if we love out hearts!

4 Wheat triggers acne and many other skin conditions.

5 Wheat has a HUGE impact on the brain and nervous system, from triggering mood swings and depression to mania in people struggling with bipolar disorder.

6 Wheat is connected to behavioural issues in children with ADD and ADHD and can trigger outbursts, meltdowns, despondence and lethargy, as well as an intense feeling of being overwhelmed in children with autism and Asperger's.

7 Gluten-free products are NOT a good alternative for a wheat-free lifestyle. Gluten-free products are made from flours with an even higher GI than wheat flour, which also causes inflammation-driven blood sugar spikes.

Wheat and grains

I wanted to write extensively on bread, wheat and modern grains, because this is where low-carb followers really tend to struggle. Some people go into a state of mourning when thinking about the departure of this item from their menus and others panic at the thought of what to feed the kids. Maybe, after reading this chapter, you might feel empowered to reconsider.

Wheat became a staple for early civilisations simply because the production of wheat meant a sustainable food source that could supply the basic needs of a growing town or city, feeding both humans and animals.

The wheat of the ancient world was very different to the wheat varieties we have today. Pieces of bread were discovered in tombs in Egypt dating back 5 000 years, and traces of einkorn and emmer wheat were found in these preserved ancient breads. Basically they were wild grasses that yielded very small amounts of wheat berries, but they were easy to cultivate. Compared to modern-day wheat varieties, einkorn and emmer wheat contain much less gluten.

We seem to have survived on wheat for a few thousand years, but that's just the problem. Our bodies are not naturally adapted to be wheat-processing factories so we merely survived on wheat, we did not excel on it.

But as the world's populations grew, so did the concern of governments to feed us.

There are currently more than 2 500 varieties of wheat. Almost every country or even region within a country has its own genetically modified version of wheat, all created in a lab. Feeding the exploding world population called for intervention methods in agriculture to yield stronger and larger crops in whatever the challenges of a certain region might be. (This is the case for all grains. Even corn and soy are extensively genetically modified.)

This was the objective. A noble one. But in our food tinkering we neglected the way the core DNA of the kernel was affected and it has led to all sorts of health havoc. This is enough reason for me to pass the bread aisle and sigh in relief.

White flour

Around the time of the Industrial Revolution, more people moved to the cities and grinding flour for most of the day was either not possible or simply not the cool thing to do. It was much easier to pop into the local bakery and get your fill.

In 1879, the first steam mill was erected in London to supply the ever-growing demand for flour. Much larger amounts could be produced in a shorter time, but the problem was that the flour had a very limited shelf life due to the reaction between the fatty acids of the wheat germ and bran when exposed to oxygen. Without the germ, however, the flour would not become rancid. So the good stuff was removed in order to eat the mostly non-essential stuff for longer. (Science for Dummies...)

At the time, white flour was much more expensive than wholewheat flour and hence became a status symbol among the upper classes. The peak in production of refined sugar and refined white flour came about almost at the same time and it was a royal marriage that gave birth to a whole new culinary experience: cakes, cookies, treats and refined breads!

In addition to the process that removes most of the nutrition from the flour, modern flours are also bleached, steamed and bombarded with chemicals.

IS WHOLEWHEAT BETTER?

Nope! Two slices of wholewheat bread will raise your blood sugar higher than 6 teaspoons of sugar. Wholewheat bread has an extremely high GI.

WHAT ABOUT MY FIBRE NEEDS?

The bran of all wheat contains something called phytic acid, which can also be explained as a mineral blocker that prevents the absorption of calcium, magnesium, iron, copper and zinc.

Rather turn to ground flaxseed, pumpkin seeds, coconut and psyllium husks in unsweetened double-cream yoghurt or smoothies or as a wheat-free, gluten-free cereal alternative. (Always drink plenty of water with fibre sources.)

Berries, broccoli, green beans, celery and cauliflower are also good sources of fibre.

WHAT EXACTLY DOES GLUTEN DO?

Gluten is a very complex protein found in the endosperm (basically the starchy part of the wheat berry they don't chuck out with the bran and the wheat germ). The word 'gluten' is Latin for glue, and it is gluten's glue-like nature that gives bread its chewy and fluffy texture and makes cakes spongy. But these glue-like properties can put our digestive tracts in a very sticky situation because it is gluten's adhesive texture that interferes with the breaking down and absorption of other nutrients in the same meal. It also ends up as a sticky mass in the gut that is hard to digest.

For someone who is gluten sensitive, this can cause inflammatory symptoms such as fatigue, brain fog, diarrhoea and joint pain, especially in the wrist joints. If someone is gluten-intolerant, however, this can lead to celiac disease, meaning their body triggers the immune system to attack the lining of the small intestine and, over time, cause digested food to leak into the bloodstream. This manifests as diarrhoea, abdominal pain, nausea or constipation.

DISEASES AND ILLNESSES LINKED TO GRAINS

- Cancers such as pancreatic, colon, stomach and lymphoma
- Autoimmune diseases such as Hashimoto's thyroiditis
- Infertility
- Diabetes
- Obesity
- Arthritis
- Autism
- Depression, anxiety and schizophrenia
- Allergies
- Alzheimer's
- Dementia
- Chronic headaches

If you're interested in reading up more about grains and how they affect the body, I can highly recommend the following two books: *Grain Brain* by Dr David Perlmutter with Kristen Loberg (published by Little, Brown and Company, 2013), and *Wheat Belly* by cardiologist Dr William Davis (published by Rodale Books, 2011).

INFLAMMATION NEWSFLASH

I am going to try and explain the basics of inflammation in very brief and broad terms because this topic is a meaty one. If you are getting ready to start an LCHF journey, you are going to feel inflammation leave your body, and it will be something to celebrate if you know how to appreciate it.

Inflammation in layman's terms is the body's defence and action response to something potentially damaging that entered or injured the body. Acute inflammation is what you get when you sprain your ankle for instance. The swelling, throbbing, redness and warmth that occurs right away is the body's way of saying, 'I'm handling it and I'm healing'.

Chronic or long-term inflammation occurs over a longer period of anything from weeks to months. There are three main things that this kind of inflammation can be trying to tell you:

- I guess we did not solve the problem surrounding the cause of the acute inflammation.
- A slight, but serious error from the autoimmune head office. This happens when the immune system mistakenly sees healthy tissue as an invader of sorts.
- There is a chronic irritant of low intensity that is overstaying its welcome in the body.

A few common examples of diseases or conditions with chronic inflammation are asthma, rheumatoid arthritis, chronic sinusitis and IBS (Irritable Bowel Syndrome). Obesity has also been linked to chronic inflammation.

To make things worse, there isn't a test for inflammation or what specifically triggers chronic inflammation. But if I had to take a guess on this one, I would say it's sugar, wheat, gluten, hydrogenated oils, non-nutritive sweeteners, preservatives, pollutants and possibly stress. It's just a wild guess, but when most people I have spoken to took these bad boys out of their diets they experienced HUGE relief!

The experts seem to agree, but also added hormonal changes, sleep deprivation and high levels of cortisol (the fight or flight stress hormone) to the list of chronic inflammation triggers.

Dr Marcelle Pick, American OB-GYN NP, author and co-founder of Women to Women Medical Clinic, has a beautiful, clear and informative approach on inflammation. In her blog she writes the following: 'At our medical practice we are convinced that the seeds of chronic inflammation (and a lot of other health issues) start with the gut. Two-thirds of the body's defenses reside in the gastrointestinal (GI) tract – yet it is often the last place traditional practitioners look.'

Standing ovation for you, doc! She also advises patients to go on an anti-inflammatory diet such as a low-carb diet and to supplement with omega-3, probiotics and unwinding with daily exercise.

HEALTHY GUT HEALTH

Prebiotics and probiotics work hand in hand to promote better gut health. Our diet needs adequate amounts of prebiotics to promote the health of the probiotic micro flora that occur naturally in our intestinal tracts.

When we are born we have neutral intestinal tracts that have to be programmed from scratch with a healthy population of gut flora. Sadly, some of our babies start this gut cultivation on highly processed, soy-filled formula milk, sugar-laden baby food and gluten-filled cereal. A baby on soy milk formula gets the hormone equivalent of four birth control pills in one day!

Kids grow up on sugar and refined carbs from their first teething biscuits to the dessert-flavoured baby food they prefer over steamed veggies. French fries with carcinogenic oils become handy finger foods and low-fat yoghurt with teaspoonsful of sugar are the go-to snack. This is the beginning years of our gut...

We should be feeding our bodies and the ones we love with good gut food!

EXAMPLES OF PREBIOTICS

Raw garlic, raw leek, raw onion, raw asparagus, broccoli, Brussels sprouts, cauliflower, kale and radish. These are all part of our low-carb staples and that is good news.

PROBIOTICS

We live in South Africa. We did not grow up with sauerkraut or miso, but we do have a wonderful probiotic superfood that has been the underdog for way too long. Let me introduce you to amasi …

Amasi is the common Zulu and Xhosa word for fermented milk that tastes a lot like plain yoghurt but with monstrous health benefits. It is packed with many different strains of gut-loving bacteria and at 5 g carbs per 100 g, it is a perfect new gutsy friend to welcome on board.

Ancient cultures thrived on naturally fermented foods and drinks. Foods were cultured instead of preserved to extend their shelf life – raw milk kefir, amasi, sauerkraut and pickles are some examples. They contain good nutrient boosts and healthy strains of bacteria that support a healthy digestive tract and inflammation fighting immune system.

To introduce amasi back into your daily diet, use it in smoothies (pp. 196–198) and salad dressings (pp. 144–145) or over low-carb cereal (pp. 39–41), and make amasi Cheese Balls (pp. 48–49), popsicles (pp. 196, 197), veggie dip, tzatziki (p. 139), guacamole and masi-sips (drinking yoghurt).

Even though amasi can be substituted in recipes calling for yoghurt or buttermilk, you need it in its original uncooked state to gain the most probiotic properties.

Now that we have covered most of the whys of low carb, from here on change is really just a few tweaks and a slight mind shift away!

Low-carb Living – The How

You are about to embark on a new and exciting journey and you should feel proud of your decision to live a low-carb lifestyle. But where do you begin?

Based on how you would have viewed meals, pantry stocking and food shopping up until now, I have compiled a breakdown for you to see what you are trading for what, food wise, which will help to make the transition so much easier. You are going to be carb smart in no time!

This system should form the basis of your practical low-carb approach when shopping or planning meals. Once you learn and understand the alternatives to bread, pasta, potatoes and rice, your low-carb lifestyle will become as normal as ever.

BE CARB SMART – 8 SIMPLE SWAP-OUTS

1 Swap sugar or honey for xylitol, stevia or erythritol. These should be used sparingly and for cooking and occasional baking only, not for coffee, tea and so on.

2 Swap all wheat, rice and potato flours for nut flours, seed flours, milled flaxseed and milled desiccated coconut. This will form the base of your new baking regime.

3 Swap veggies that grow beneath the ground, as well as high-carb peas, corn and legumes, for other veggies that grow above the ground.

4 Swap rice, mashed potatoes and pastas for cauliflower 'rice', veggie mash and cabbage strips sautéed in butter.

5 Swap bad hydrogenated fats, seed oils and margarine for good fats such as cream, butter, olive oil, coconut oil, avocado and avocado oil, eggs, cheese, animal fats and coconut milk or cream. Use daily as your primary source of energy.

6 Swap cereal, processed snacks and candies for *Low Carb is Lekker* recipes, nuts and seeds (a small child's handful and NO peanuts), low-carb fruits, occasional 85% cocoa dark chocolate.

7 Swap processed meat and cereal-filled polony for fatty, if possible grass-fed, juicy meat (rind, fat and skin still on), quality salami, bacon, roast beef, chicken, fish, organs and marrowbones.

8 Swap sugary drinks for sparkling water.

OH SUGAR!

It is only carbohydrates that affect blood sugar and insulin levels to any significant degree, which is why we use a low-carb high-fat (LCHF) approach instead.

All forms of sugar, even molasses and agave, have a very high glyceamic index (GI). But what is GI? GI measures the effect that carbohydrates have on blood sugar levels. A carbohydrate-dense food that quickly releases glucose into the bloodstream as it breaks down during digestion is said to have a high GI. Fibre-rich foods that take longer to release glucose tend to have a lower GI. Fat and protein are seen as no GI.

The following comparisons are an example of the general carbohydrate spread and are listed according to global standards:

0–55 = low GI (Examples: flaxseed, nuts, berries, apples, veggies, legumes, barley, millet)

56–69 = medium GI (Examples: bananas, oats, brown rice, honey, table sugar)

70 and above = high GI (Examples: white bread, white rice, glucose, potatoes, breakfast cereals)

If you and your family functioned in the medium and high brackets, your insulin levels had a daily roller coaster ride and snacking would likely occur often as the body's way of trying to stabilise things.

I must point out that 55 GI is still very high, all things considered. Aim for foods that are less than 10 GI, which covers almost all above-ground veggies, nuts and seeds.

Xylitol and **erythritol** are sugar alcohols and are absorbed in the body in a very different way to sugar. They are not fully absorbed by the gut and mostly pass through the system without much impact, according to most studies and sources. They are natural and safe to use but their consumption should still be limited. Pigging out on them will negatively affect weight loss and I would suggest you use them ONLY in baking treats a few times a week and NOT in coffee or tea.

Of the two, I prefer organic xylitol, which is made from birch bark and has a low GI of 7. It really is a pleasure to bake with and brings a wonderful sense of normalcy without the spike! Note, however, that overconsumption can have a laxative effect.

WARNING: Food containing xylitol should never be fed to dogs.

Erythritol is not widely available yet in South Africa, but works just as well as xylitol and has a much lower GI. Sugar alcohols (nothing to do with actual alcohol) do have some empty kilojoules, much like regular sugar, but it does not cause a rapid spike in blood glucose and has little to no effect on insulin levels.

Stevia is a natural plant sweetener that is 300 times sweeter than sugar. It is 100 per cent natural with no kilojoules and NO effect on blood sugar. It does, however, have an aftertaste that some may dislike and it's also harder to determine how much to use in recipes.

I have found stevia to be a better alternative to use in drinks as you can sweeten without the added kilojoules. I add 1–2 tsp xylitol to 8 cups liquid and then sweeten to taste with stevia to balance the taste. **PLEASE NOTE: It is never a good idea to take in your daily kilojoules through drinks. Rather eat real food and fuel your body wisely!**

Here is a handy sugar GI comparison. (If you read meat labels you will be surprised to see how often the first three names on this list pop up. Sugar hides in interesting places, folks!)

Maltodextrin	Sugar	110
Maltose	Sugar	105
Dextrose	Sugar	100
Glucose	Sugar	100
Sucrose	Sugar	65
Golden syrup	Modified sugar	60
Inverted sugar	Modified sugar	60
Blackstrap molasses	Sugar extract	55
Honey	Natural sugar	55–75
Coconut palm sugar	Natural sugar	35
Maltitol	Sugar alcohol	35
Fructose	Sugar	25
Agave syrup	Modified sugar	15
Xylitol (organic)	Sugar alcohol	7
Erythritol	Sugar alcohol	1
Stevia	Natural sugar	0

A NUTTY AFFAIR

This section – where you swap out wheat, rice and potato flours for nut and seed flours – is probably the one that takes the most getting used to, but it is also the section that is not desperately needed for our existence, so you can ease into it.

Isn't it good to know that your LCHF lifestyle can still include 'decarbed' bread, cookies, muffins and cereal? You just need to approach it from a different, very viable angle.

The bottom line is this: wheat is a seed that is ground into flour. Using this same basic concept, you can grind any seed or nut into flour.

How to make your own nut butters, nut flours and seed meals

My coffee grinder is my BEST kitchen friend for this very reason. Any nut can be ground into flour, and the best thing is that you can use virtually any nut or seed to make the flour needed for a recipe, which is very handy when the price or availability of the suggested ingredient becomes an issue. As long as you stay clear from cashews and peanuts. They are actually legumes with a higher GI and carb count than the rest. The rest of the nut kingdom is yours to explore!

My favourites are pecan nuts and almonds. Macadamias tend to have a higher oil content and might start to turn into a paste in your grinder, but upon mixing in the rest of the ingredients they will become a batter as good as any other.

Flour is usually seen as ground nuts without the skin, while **meal** is regarded as ground nuts with the skin. Both will give you good baking results.

Seed meal

Some days I add a blend of flaxseed, pumpkin seeds, desiccated coconut and sunflower seeds into my coffee grinder and make a lovely nutrient-rich base flour that I use for literally anything from muffins to buns to cookies. It simply is flour in the end and can help to stretch the budget a bit too.

Otherwise just use the seeds a specific recipe asks for and grind for 10–20 seconds. Always measure afterwards to have the exact amount and sift into the dry ingredients.

Coconut meal

I make my own coconut flour/meal by adding some desiccated coconut into my coffee grinder, enough to completely cover the blade. Grind for 10–15 seconds. It actually has a lower carb count than commercially available, ready-made coconut flour too.

Nut meal

Nut meal is ground from nuts with the skin on. When grinding, make sure to fill the grinder up to capacity, otherwise if the nuts have too much room to move, some tend to stay in bigger chunks. Grind in two spurts of 10 seconds each. Measure and sift.

If convenience is your thing, you can buy ready-made almond and coconut flours. The good news is that they are becoming more readily available at most supermarkets, but health stores always stock them. If budget and availability talks louder, then bring on the coffee grinder!

And for those who only want to bake something once in a while and don't want to hunt down all the seeds and nuts, simply walk into your nearest supermarket and buy a 100 g packet of ground almonds from the dried fruit aisle. This makes up roughly 1 cup of ready-made flour.

Nut butter

1 cup nut meal
2 Tbsp coconut oil
2 Tbsp olive oil
1 tsp xylitol
1 Tbsp tahini (optional)

Use a stick blender and blend all the ingredients together until smooth and creamy.

Yields about 1 cup at 14 g carbs per cup.

Baking with nut flours and seed meals

I prefer to bake with nuts instead of eating them whole. My reason for this is simple: if there is a jar of spicy nut mix standing on my kitchen counter, my family will snack on it by the handful and consume much more than they need. (This causes many a weight stall too.)

When I bake with nuts, I can give my family a treat, such as a brownie, which relates to 1 cup of nuts divided between four to six portions. This is a bit more carb smart and budget smart too.

In my experience, almond meal or flour works best for lighter sponge cake-based baked goods, such as cupcakes, vanilla cakes, and so on. Pecan meal works well in recipes where you would have previously used nutty wheat or wholewheat flours, for example for muffins, breads and rusks. And pumpkin seed meal works wonders when used in any recipe that also has cocoa in the ingredient list.

Just note that due to the high oil content in nut meal or flour, recipes such as rusks don't dry out exactly like commercial wheat flour-based rusks, but they are still 'dip-able' and comforting. For this reason (and the absence of sugar) cookies too are generally chewier and softer instead of crunchy.

Why use psyllium husks in baking?

Another foreign little wonder to your baking regime will be psyllium husk fibre. It's a no-carb fibre that almost becomes like a gelling agent the moment it's combined with a liquid. It really improves baking by leaps and bounds, standing in for gluten but without the nasties. Psyllium also brings a beautiful, much needed fibre boost into a low-carb lifestyle.

Ingredient decoder

Almond flour: Flour made from blanched almonds. Use a coffee grinder.

Almond meal: Flour made from raw almonds (skin on). Use a coffee grinder.

Pecan meal: Flour made from pecan nuts (skin on). Use a coffee grinder.

Pumpkin seed meal: Flour made from pumpkin seeds. Use a coffee grinder. This is a great budget option compared to some nut flours. Find a good bulk supplier.

Flax meal/Ground flaxseed: Flour made from flaxseed. Use a coffee grinder. Because of the high omega-3 content flax meal can turn rancid quickly, so grind and use the meal within a day or two or store in the refrigerator for up to a week. Rather try to grind the required amount into a fresh meal for best omega benefits. The seeds can be stored for a long time. Find a good bulk supplier.

Desiccated coconut (fine): Available in standard store packaging, fine shred option.

Desiccated coconut (medium): Available in standard store packaging, medium shred option.

Coconut meal: Finer flour made from grinding desiccated coconut in a coffee grinder. This is a budget substitute for expensive coconut flours and I use this throughout this book.

Coconut chips: Larger coconut flakes or shavings.

Psyllium husk fibre: Available in standard store packaging. Has a fine powder consistency.

Psyllium husks: Available in standard store packaging. Has a more fibrous husk consistency.

Psyllium powder: Powder made from grinding psyllium husks in a coffee grinder.

Stores currently don't really differentiate between the two. The finer powder is always better for baking, otherwise just buy what you can find and whizz the amount of husks the recipe calls for in your coffee grinder to make sure it is nice and fine.

VEGGIES

Veggies and leafy greens – the brighter the better – that grow above the ground are generally safe to consume in abundance without having to count carbs. Overall they offer you fibre and nutrients galore, are less than 5 g carbs per 100 g and are very low on the GI scale.

Vegetables that grow below the ground have been cultivated over the last few hundred years to yield better crops and have a starchy sweetness that works well for mash or fries. Unfortunately they have lost the fibrous element that brings down the carb count. (Ideally it is good to consume veggies with a nett carb count – carbs minus fibre, because fibre does not add to the usable carbs – of less than 5 g carbs per 100 g.)

Boiled potato: 18 g carbs per 100 g
Baked sweet potato: 17 g carbs per 100 g
Parsnips: 12.5 g carbs per 100 g
Beetroot: 7.5 g carbs per 100 g

The following veggies also grow below ground but are not as high in carbs and can be enjoyed sparingly:
Baby carrots: 6 g carbs per 100 g
Large carrots: 4.9 g carbs per 100 g
Onions: 7.9 g carbs per 100 g
Turnips: 4.5 g carbs per 100 g
Radishes: 2 g carbs per 100 g

There are some veggies that grow above ground that have a fairly high GI and it would be smart to limit them to 'occasional' status:
Garden peas: 11.3 g carbs per 100 g
Leeks: 12 g carbs per 100 g
Butternut: 10 g carbs per 100 g
Pumpkin: 6 g carbs per 100 g

Gem squash is safe at 3.3 g carbs per 100 g and **Hubbard squash** can be regularly enjoyed at 4.8 g carbs per 100 g.

Corn is technically NOT a veggie (it is a grain), but in South Africa people see and treat corn on the cob as a veggie. Limit its consumption to 'hardly ever'.

Corn: 17 g carbs per 100 g

Because LCHF is a lifestyle, eat as much variety as you can. Your body needs a wide nutrient base.

CARB-BUSTER CREW

It really is quite simple to cut out carbs once you understand that they DON'T form the substance of a meal, they simply bulk it up. With the right nutrition there is no need to bulk up a meal.

As soon as you remove the empty nutrition and sugar-spiking and craving-causing part of a meal, your metabolism will begin to heal and will naturally regulate your appetite. Trust me, you WILL feel full without the carbs.

You also don't need to buy more food to replace the pasta, rice or potatoes. You will, however, buy these more often: cabbage, cauliflower, spinach, baby marrows, green beans and pumpkin.

As soon as you understand this very crucial swap concept, your meal combos will feel 'normal' again in no time.

You will make the most amazing mash (p. 127) using different combinations of cauliflower and marrows, cauliflower and green beans or cauliflower and spinach. Ooze in a knob of butter, salt and pepper and eat like a king!

Fried Cabbage Strips (p. 127) can easily take the place of lasagne, pasta or rice. I have also included some 'decarbed' classics in the recipe section so there is no reason to feel deprived of these familiar favourites!

FAT (YOUR NEW BFF)

Embracing healthy fat is by far the hardest switch for many. The fact that your body stores fat and not carbs or protein, should be a clear indication of what our body's preferred fuelling system really is.

I used to cringe at the thought of fat. Melting butter in the pan to fry eggs in it... I almost did not make it. I saw exploding hearts and several frowning school teachers wherever I looked. The irony is, a few years into my family's low-carb journey, we've had to deal with broken hearts and heartache, but NEVER an exploding heart! In fact, our cholesterol readings are at textbook levels.

Fat is the most concentrated form of nutritional energy. It's like rocket fuel compared to carbohydrates. But contrary to popular myth, you will not be eating a block of butter a day. You use very little actually. You also cannot ignore this part of the lifestyle because you feel grossed out or scared – you need to embrace healthy fats to fuel your energy and keep your blood sugar levels stable!

The veggies or small portion of low-carb fruit you eat have a much bigger chance of spiking your blood sugar than the butter with your fried egg. Overconsumption of protein in one sitting can also cause a sugar spike, but fat ... not a chance!

As a family, we have worked out that we eat less fat on an LCHF diet than we would have consumed had we added all the extra junk and hydrogenated oils in chips, flaky pie crusts, margarine, chocolate bars and processed foods from our pre-LCHF journey. The fats we consume with LCHF are high quality, nutritious fuel.

The biggest mind shift that needs to happen is that you understand that you cannot pig out on fat. You will feel full before you can even think about it. That's the beauty of fuelling wisely.

And remember, the things that made you over-indulge (wheat and sugar) have been banned from your pantry anyway!

Heat-stable fats for cooking and frying
- Coconut oil
- Butter
- Lard, tallow or duck fat

Coconut oil and butter contain saturated fats that our bodies can digest easily. They supply us with instant energy and they are great for fat loss.

Fats for cold use only
- Extra virgin olive oil
- Macadamia oil
- Avocado oil
- Fish oil

These oils are high in omega-9 and are known to prevent heart disease.

Fats to avoid
- Margarine
- Canola oil
- Sunflower oil
- Safflower
- Cottonseed
- Soybean
- Grape seed oil
- Corn oil

These oils are severely hydrogenated and pro-cessed, often made from genetically modified seeds, are pro-inflammatory, are bad for your gut health and they increase bad cholesterol and re-duce concentrations of good cholesterol.

SENSIBLE SNACKS
This recipe book was designed with sensible snacks in mind and should give you a good variety of 'de-carbed' treats to share with the entire family. You need to know that these low-carb treats are deca-dent in EVERY way! However, if you eat some store-bought pretzels inbetween, your body will burn the carbs first and store the rest as fat. So stick to low-carb snacks only – no switching between low-carb and traditional snacks.

Cut the carbs and fuel wisely. Whether a meal or a treat, food is fuel. Living a LCHF lifestyle means we shouldn't eat because we are bored. We eat to function optimally. To sit on a couch and watch television while eating handfuls of nuts or biltong means either you did not eat enough to keep you satisfied for six hours or you just aren't listening to your body telling you, 'Thanks for the fatty good-ness during dinner.'

A treat in our house is often seen as a meal or we eat a smaller portion at dinner in order to allow for a nutrient-dense dessert as part of one 'fuelling stop'. Our treats consist of nutrient-dense ingredi-ents such as nuts, cream, eggs and butter.

Enjoy these treats, see them as fuel within the bigger picture and you will be carb-smart, healthy and content.

MEATY MATTERS
Quality meat cuts really matter in a low-carb lifestyle. It makes no sense to eliminate all the inflammation-causing grains and sugars from our diets and then eat animals that were raised on those same GMO, hormone-filled products. Even if you can just start with some good sources of meat and phase in the rest, it will make a big difference already.

When it comes to meat, try to stick to the fol-lowing guidelines:

1 LCHF is not a high-protein diet. The quality of the meat is more important than the quantity.

2 Find a few friends or households that will share half a grass-fed beef, free-range lamb or acorn-

raised pork with you. You will be surprised at how much you save compared to buying smaller, expensive, lower quality portions in stores.

3 Visit farmers' markets for free-range chickens and eggs if you can. Whatever you can get without hormones is a great start. Ease into it. Don't feel overwhelmed, but be aware of what you eat.

4 Eat a bigger variety of meat cuts and not just the muscle parts. Most of the good stuff is in the bones and the fatty offcuts. Stewing meats are great examples. The gelatine found in animal bones is a much-overlooked super food and so are free-range organs. They are also good news for the budget!

BASIC BEVERAGES

Don't drink your carbs. Much of our obesity state is due to this factor. If you love your kids, don't give them boxed fruit juice. All fruit juices, even freshly squeezed ones, are concentrated carbs (fructose) without the much-needed fibre to help your body absorb it slower. In addition, you use much more than one piece of fruit to yield 1 cup of juice, meaning you take in more in fruit juice than you would have been able to eat in whole fruit in one sitting.

Carbs in 1 cup boxed fruit juice:
Apple juice: 29 g carbs, of which 0.2% is fibre; the rest is sugar
Grape juice: 38 g carbs, of which 0.3% is fibre; the rest is sugar
Orange juice: 26 g carbs, of which 0.5% is fibre; the rest is sugar

Without the fibre, fruit juice becomes an inflammation-driving sugar spike just waiting for a place to happen. Not to mention the additives and preservatives.

Rather give your children water (and serve it in a cute container). For variation, add some frozen fruit as ice cubes and for added flavour.

For the juicers out there:
1 cup carrot juice has 22 g carbs – 2 grams fibre = 20 g carbs

DAIRY

One cup of milk has 11 g carbs. This is fine for kids, but if you are trying to lose weight, drinking glasses of milk will quickly use up your day's carb allowance.

Overall, diet soda should be avoided and never introduced as a regular in the home refrigerator. However, socially it is often the only drink option at a gathering or event. *Save your diet soda credits ONLY for such occasions and never for domestic consumption.

Our country has the most wonderful home-grown tea blends. See the Beverage chapter (p. 194) for healthy ice tea alternatives.

ALCOHOL AND A LOW-CARB LIFESTYLE

If losing weight isn't your main goal, a modest serving of alcohol can be enjoyed from time to time. If weight loss is your goal, however, avoid alcohol altogether as it slows down fat burning.

Best low-carb alcohol options are:

1 Quality red wine has the biggest health benefit to carb ratio. It contains resveratrol, a powerful antioxidant with anti-aging and cancer-fighting properties. 1 x 150 ml serving = 3–5 g carbs

2 Wood-aged whiskey has a potent amount of free radical fighters. 0 g carbs

3 Vodka, gin, rum, tequila, brandy, cognac = 0 g carbs, but only if you enjoy them occasionally – straight or with water or soda water.

4 White wine does not have any significant health benefits. 1 x 150 ml serving = 3–5 g carbs

5 Champagne or sparkling wine: 1 x 150 ml serving = 1.5 g carbs

THE GOOD, THE BAD AND THE UGLY: FOODS TO ENJOY AND THOSE TO AVOID

LCHF should have actually been called 'the stable blood sugar lifestyle', because this is really what it boils down to: avoiding spikes in blood sugar levels at all costs!

Secondly, a low-carb lifestyle is about eating your way around unnecessary inflammation and into healthy metabolism.

Allow Always

BEVERAGES

- Homemade ice teas, lemonades, sparkling water, water
- Tea, coffee (substitute milk with cream if you drink more than 3 cups a day)

MEATS

- Grass-fed meats (if possible)
- Venison, ostrich
- Free-range animal organs
- Biltong, droëwors, quality salami, Parma ham, roast beef
- Fish
- Seafood
- Free-range chicken (if possible)

HEALTHY FATS

- Flaxseed (mill a fresh omega-filled batch often)
- Avocado
- Free-range eggs (if possible)
- Cream cheese
- Olive oil, avocado oil, macadamia oil
- Bone broths
- Coconut milk or coconut cream
- Coconut oil
- Desiccated coconut

NUTS AND SEEDS

- Basic bread and rolls (pp. 146–152)
- Pumpkin seeds, flaxseed, mixed seeds

DAIRY

- Butter
- Fresh cream
- Variety of cheese, cream cheese
- Amasi

VEGGIES

- All leafy green veggies and herbs
- All kinds of lettuce, tomatoes, avocado, celery
- Cauliflower, broccoli, asparagus, baby marrows, patty pans
- All kinds of cabbage (but not Brussels sprouts), sauerkraut
- Green beans, green pepper, red pepper, chillies
- Mushrooms, spring onions, olives
- Hubbard squash, gem squash, brinjals
- Mange tout, sugar snap peas, radishes and cucumber

FRUIT (5 g CARBS OR LESS PER SPECIFIED PORTION)

- 1 medium guava
- 6–7 whole strawberries
- 1 whole apricot
- 1 small peach
- 2 granadillas
- 1 naartjie
- 1 prickly pear
- ½ cup blackberries
- ½ cup raspberries
- ¼ cup blueberries

Keep track of your fruit intake. If you use some in a smoothie, try not to grab another portion as is. Try to stick with 1 portion a day. Children can do 1 or 2 a day of these.

CONDIMENTS

- Fresh garlic and ginger
- Sugar-free herb and spice mixes
- Spices and sugar-free BBQ blends
- Lemon or lime juice, fresh or bottled (1 g carbs per Tbsp)
- Bay leaves
- Lime leaves
- Gluten-free Thai curry pastes
- Homemade low-carb condiments in this book (pp. 136–140)
- Salad dressings from this book (pp. 144–145)
- Apple cider vinegar and wine vinegars
- Unsweetened Dijon mustard and English mustard
- Sugar-free bottled hot sauces, such as Tabasco®
- Fresh salsas, pestos, guacamole, horseradish, capers

Allow Sometimes

BEVERAGES
- Smoothies
- Hot chocolates
- Hot toddies

NUTS
- Baked treats
- Whole nuts

DAIRY
- Dessert mousse (p. 163)
- Plain double-cream yoghurt

VEGGIES
- Pumpkin
- Onion
- Carrot
- Yellow pepper
- Leeks

FRUIT (PORTIONS OF NOT MORE THAN 10 g CARBS)
- 1 cup whole strawberries or raspberries
- ½ cup whole blueberries or blackberries
- ½ cup grapes
- 1 whole plum
- ½ medium apple
- ½ orange
- ½ cup honeydew melon or cantaloupe
- 1 kiwi fruit
- 1 cup sliced watermelon

Allow Seldom

- 85% dark chocolate
- Balsamic vinegar
- Worcestershire sauce
- Wine
- Butternut
- Peas
- Nut butter
- Diet soda*

Avoid

- All processed foods, snacks, condiments
- All artificial sweeteners
- All jams and jellies
- All wheat flours and wholewheat products
- All grains and grain-based flours
- All gluten-free products
- All rice, potatoes, pasta, couscous, lentils, dried beans, soup mixes, corn and popcorn
- All processed meats, Viennas, ham, polony
- All soy products (even baby formula)
- Pickled ginger and commercially pickled foods with added sugars
- Soda and diet soda*, sweetened milk, commercial drinking yoghurts and ice teas
- All energy drinks
- All fruit juice (except lemon and lime juice)
- Whole, high-GI fruit portions, such as bananas, dates
- High-GI fruits such as raisins and other dried fruit
- Peanut butter
- Cashews
- Honey and molasses
- Agave
- Fructose
- Yeast
- Soup powders and stock cubes
- Cornstarch (cornflour)
- Low-fat products
- Cereals, baby cereals
- Beer
- Candy
- Commercial ice cream
- Creamers and artificial cream
- All sugar and all foods with added sugar

At restaurants avoid
- Basting sauces (ask for food to be prepared without it)
- Potatoes, veggies filled with sugar
- Sweetened salad dressings
- Foods in crumbs or batters
- Ask if they use butter or margarine and ask them to omit if they use margarine

Why the following should be avoided

Legumes: Quite high in carbs and could limit nutrition absorption. Not significantly high in protein either. Medium fibre.

Potatoes: Sugar spike will follow consumption.

Artificial sweeteners: There is growing research that links artificial sweeteners to certain cancers and, contrary to popular marketing strategies, artificial sweeteners still impact insulin levels.

Soup powders: High in starch and preservatives. This could trigger sugar spike, inflammation and lead to cravings.

Cornstarch: Very high GI.

Popcorn: It's a GMO grain. High GI.

Fruit: Needs to be treated as nature's candies and consumed in moderation.

Soy sauce: Hormone filled, GMO, also contains gluten and preservatives.

Commercial spices: More sugar and gluten than herbs and natural spices. Check labels carefully or find natural ranges.

Commercial marinades and condiments: Filled with sugar, starches and hydrogenated oils.

Seed oils: Hydrogenated, DNA modification in order to get from seed to oil. Toxins and free radicals released when heated.

Margarine: Much too high in inflammation-causing omega-6. Highly processed; not a real food at all!

Gluten-free products: They are made with high-GI flours and are not sugar free either.

Foods that could stall weight loss

These foods could have little to no effect on one person but turn into an ugly culprit for the next. There are two reasons for this: you might have an underlying food allergy, or the food itself is not the problem, but rather the portion size is. It is easy to over eat on nuts and yoghurt.

- Whole nuts
- Wine
- Double-cream yoghurt
- Dairy products such as cheese and milk
- Fruit
- Too much protein

LOW CARB FOR THE WHOLE FAMILY – A BALANCED, SUSTAINABLE APPROACH

If I've done a good job with this book, I shouldn't need to do much convincing that LCHF is a lifestyle that benefits the whole family.

It saddens me to hear how adults use the LCHF lifestyle benefits of weight loss or sport performance for themselves, while still allowing their children to eat harmful foods.

As parents, we are the gatekeepers of our families. If sugar is not good for you, it is not good for your children. If living grain free benefits you, it will also benefit them.

By cutting out wheat and sugar, appetites in your household will go from monster- to mouse-size within the first few weeks. This also dispels the myth that LCHF is expensive. It will NOT break the bank.

Hopefully, you are reading this because you want the best health for yourself and your loved ones. Because my approach to this lifestyle is NOT a diet, rather a sustainable everyday way of life, you should find plenty of ways to swap commercially loved foods for 'decarbed' goodness. It is also one of the main reasons why I wrote this book, so that this generation can understand and teach the following generation. Low-carb living is a healthy, sustainable option for the whole family.

Here are a few practical pointers to keep in mind when taking the plunge with your family:

1 Babies start out as low-carbers naturally, it's parents and grandparents who feed them and teach them otherwise. Processed and sugary foods were created to establish a market that desires more. It's the way money makes this world go round. If you introduce your child to processed foods and sugar at a young age, it will awaken the addiction from which you are now struggling to break free.

2 Educate your children. My page and website has a few kiddie-friendly video clips you can watch with them. Go to http://lowcarbislekker.wordpress.com to find out more.

3 Most of the kids who are at school with your children or who are friends with them are not on a low-carb lifestyle. Establish a healthy low-carb regime at home and don't stress about the occasional cupcake or birthday cake they get at school or a party. Such is life.

4 Have a commercial treat outing once a month or so. It is important that your child learns how to make socially smart food choices independently. Rather allow them to choose a hamburger with you than finding junk food behind your back. At least when the meltdown comes after a milkshake you can be present in the teaching moment!

5 Don't make a big deal about your lifestyle being different. Just focus on it being the new normal. We are not driven by our desire for food. We are simply fuelled by food. Food is not a reward. Food can always incorporate a celebration. And then we choose the best food! We manage food, not the other way around. Children follow well, especially if you are enthusiastic about the process.

6 For optimal weight loss results and blood sugar stability, several medical professionals recommend no more than 30 g of carbs a day. This is important for adults and only for children who need to follow a strict ketogenic diet for medical conditions such as epilepsy. Overall, children can tolerate more carbs than adults. It is okay for them to have a cup of milk or a smoothie daily, or more portions of fruit and a small baked treat a day. They don't need to be concerned about weight loss, just about healthy fuelling. The principle for children is purely one of being carb-smart and well nourished. And a bunch of empty carbs from commercial breads and pastas are not optimal fuel!

ALLERGY ALTERNATIVES

Dairy, egg and nut substitutes

1 Replace any NUT flour or meal with pumpkin seed meal, coconut meal or flax meal. If you replace nut flour with coconut meal, add another egg and 3 Tbsp of liquid to the recipe.

2 Replace BUTTER with melted or soft coconut oil.

3 Replace milk, cream, amasi, sour cream or yoghurt with coconut milk or coconut cream.

4 Replace eggs with egg replacer (available from health stores), NOT egg substitute.

KITCHEN MUST-HAVES

A coffee grinder!

You will make tons of your own flour. A regular coffee grinder has a grinding capacity of 50 g per grind. That means two grinding sessions of 20 seconds each will give you a lovely fresh cup of nut meal, coconut meal or seed meal. 100 g = about 1 cup flour.

All that's left for you to do is measure and sift into your dry ingredients. Say goodbye to expensive store flours. Now you can buy whatever fits your budget better.

Stick blender

A stick blender is a daily kitchen buddy. I use one that doubles up as an electric mixer simply by switching the heads. You will use this handy piece of equipment for everything from making purées, mash, soups, tomato sauce, mayonnaise and smoothies to whipping cream, icing and creaming eggs and xylitol for batters.

Blender

A glass jug blender is handy to purée larger batches of soups and family-sized smoothies made with frozen fruits and ice cubes.

A stovetop-to-oven pan and casserole

Some dishes start out being browned on the stovetop and thereafter need to cook for a few minutes or hours in the oven. The Breakfast Pizza (p. 44) is a good example; it would be an absolute nightmare to try and dish the pizza into an oven-proof dish while still fairly liquid.

Food processor

To make coleslaw, cauli-rice, cauli-couscous, salsa, guacamole, cheesecake batter, and so on.

Ice-cream maker

Because no one else will be able to offer you ice cream as cheap, lekker and 100 per cent low-carb approved! I have included three ice-cream recipes for you to try (p. 165).

Silicone cake moulds

A 12-hole muffin tray, cake ring mould, round cake mould and a loaf pan are ideal. A non-stick brownie pan (divided into compartments) is also a great investment and worth considering.

HOW TO READ FOOD LABELS

Reading labels might feel like a new hobby to you for a while, but it can be very insightful. Other than recognising how cleverly sugar and hydrogenated oil and starches are hidden everywhere, you will also discover the real impact of the food.

Start by reading the carbohydrates contained in a 100-g-portion first. Then check the fibre content. You need to subtract the fibre from the carbs to determine the actual carbs that will impact blood sugar. That is the most important information. For example, if the carbohydrates of the food item are 14 g per 100 g but it has a fibre content of 5.5 g, then the real impact or nett carbs will be 8.5 g.

Any food with a carb count of 5 g or less per 100 g is an excellent choice. Any food below 15 g nett carbs is okay for most people and will not trigger a big insulin reaction.

Usually it is safe to keep a meal below this level too. Some treats can almost reach this carb count and should be regarded as a meal instead. It's unlikely you would feel the need to eat anything else after enjoying a piece of my Chocolate Crème de la Crème Cake (p. 168) anyway!

If a label has a low nett carb count but contains artificial sweeteners and cottonseed oils, avoid it. You deserve better than that.

WHAT TO STOCK

Pantry

1 Out with the old, in with the new. Start by removing everything from your kitchen that falls into any of the 'Avoid' categories (p. 32).

2 Rearrange your cupboard to help you reach your everyday staples quickly. This will also make it easier to see when something needs to be replaced.

SPICES

Sea salt, ground cinnamon, ground ginger, turmeric, mild curry powder, ground coriander, allspice, peppercorns, ground cumin, paprika, garlic and parsley salt, natural salt and spice grinders, sugar-free barbecue spice, garlic flakes, chilli flakes, coriander seeds, whole cloves, mustard powder, cardamom.

OTHER

Apple cider vinegar, olive oil, olives, tomato purée, tomato and onion mix, whole peeled tomatoes in tomato juice, coconut milk, coconut cream, Thai curry paste, dried lime leaves, coconut oil, biltong, droëwors.

BAKING SHELF

Baking powder, vanilla extract, bicarbonate of soda, cream of tartar, bovine gelatine, cocoa powder, xylitol, debittered stevia powder or liquid, psyllium husk fibre, Simply Delish natural jellies, small slab Lindt 85% dark chocolate, Caring Candies™ bars (for choc chips), Caring Candies™ Frutz (for sprinkles).

If you are very gluten sensitive, you might want to note that regular baking powder contains a very small amount of cornstarch in order to keep it from clumping. You can make your own gluten-free baking powder and store it in an airtight container for about a month at a time. (The carb counts of the store bought and homemade baking powders don't differ much though. In fact, the homemade baking powder has a slightly higher carb count due to the amount of cream of tartar present in the mixture.)

GLUTEN-FREE BAKING POWDER
1 part bicarbonate of soda
2 parts cream of tartar

Mix the amounts practical for your home baking needs and store in an airtight container. Use the same amounts as you would for regular baking powder.

NUTS AND SEEDS (STORED IN AIRTIGHT JARS)
- 1 kg each pumpkin seeds and flaxseed
- 2 kg whole nuts (at least two varieties)
- 500 g blanched almonds (optional)
- 400 g seed mix
- 100 g each poppy seeds and sesame seeds
- 200 g sunflower mix
- 200 g psyllium husk fibre

COCONUT (STORED IN AIRTIGHT JARS)
- 1 kg fine desiccated coconut
- 1 kg coconut chips
- 200 g medium desiccated coconut

Refrigerator
CEREAL (STORED IN AN AIRTIGHT JAR)
- 1 quantity Almost Instant Breakfast Cereal (p. 40)

BASIC BREAD READY MIX (ENOUGH FOR 7 DAYS)
Mix the dry ingredients of 2–3 quantities Basic Bread (p. 147) in advance and store in an airtight container.

FOUR-SEEDS BREAD
Mix the dry ingredients of 2–3 quantities Four-seeds Bread (p. 152) in advance and store in an airtight container.

- 1 quantity salad dressing (pp. 144–145) (enough for 7 days)
- 1 quantity Creamy Mayo (p. 139) (enough for 7 days)
- 1 quantity Tomato Sauce (p. 136) (enough for 7 days)
- 1 quantity Cherry Tomato and Ginger Jam (p. 136) (enough for 14 days)
- 1 quantity Berry Jam (p. 136) (enough for 14 days)
- 1 litre amasi or 1 litre double-cream yoghurt
- 1 x 230 g block cream cheese
- 1 litre fresh cream
- Cheese and cheese cubes of your choice
- Full-cream milk
- Simple Syrup for cool drinks (p. 193)
- 2 litres Homemade Iced Tea (p. 194)
- Lard and butter
- Eggs
- Water
- Veggies of choice
- Veggie strips prepared for handy snacks and lunchboxes
- Cold cuts of choice
- Pesto
- Nut butter
- Fruit

Freezer
- Frozen berries
- Frozen ready-prepared *Low-carb is lekker* recipes, such as meatballs, buns, breads, muffins, treats
- Meat cuts, fish, chicken, marrowbones, breakfast meats and bulk nuts (optional)
- Extra butter blocks
- 4 x 1 litre containers fresh cream (to be thawed at room temperature)
- Bone broth frozen in bags
- Soup made in bulk
- Extra smoothie mix poured into popsicle moulds
- Frozen yoghurt cups ready to pop into a lunchbox

Lastly, start a beautiful tea collection on your countertop or in a tea caddy, and fill a basket with avocados, lemons, limes, your low-carb fruit picks for the week and a glass of fresh herbs.

Breakfast

Cinnamon crunch

AFTER READING OODLES OF CEREAL BOXES IN SEARCH OF SOME FORM OF FAMILIAR BUT LOW-CARB CEREAL OPTION,
MY DAUGHTER TOOK A PACKET OF COCONUT FLAKES FROM THE CUPBOARD AND TOLD ME THAT IF YOU GET CORN FLAKES,
WHY NOT COCONUT FLAKES?

½ cup coconut flakes (available
from Dis-Chem, Montagu stores
and fruit and nut suppliers)
⅓ cup pumpkin seeds (use them
whole or mill them)
⅓ cup flaxseed
1 tsp xylitol (optional)
¼ tsp ground cinnamon
⅓ cup fresh cream or amasi
4 Tbsp boiling water (if you prefer
your cereal warm)

Toast the coconut and pumpkin seeds in a dry pan until some of the flakes are aromatic and a rich brown colour.

Grind the whole flaxseed in a coffee grinder and add to the pan to heat up slightly. Add the xylitol and cinnamon and allow to infuse with the rest of the ingredients.

Now, dish into two bowls, add the cream and hot water, stir and enjoy! Omit the hot water if you prefer a cold, crunchy cereal.

Yields 2 servings at around 5 g carbs per serving.

LEKKER TIPS

- Add a couple of sliced strawberries, blackberries or raspberries to liven things up a bit.
- For dairy intolerance, swap the dairy for coconut milk.

COCONUT is our long-lost, dear friend! It speeds up metabolism, is LOW GI and GENTLE on blood sugar levels. It's uber-high in fibre, COMBATS CRAVINGS, super-charges your ENERGY LEVELS and PROTECTS against heart disease and diabetes.

DID YOU KNOW? Coconut contains no trans-fats, is GLUTEN-FREE, non-toxic, hypo-allergenic, and also contains antibacterial, ANTIVIRAL, antifungal and antiparasitic healing properties. Coconut aids and supports overall IMMUNE SYSTEM FUNCTIONS.

Krummelpap

PAP IS A PORRIDGE MADE FROM MAIZE (CORN) MEAL AND IS THE STAPLE FOOD OF SOUTHERN AFRICA. PUTUPAP IS ALSO KNOWN AS KRUMMELPAP, WHICH MEANS 'CRUMBLY PORRIDGE'. IT IS MADE WITH VERY LITTLE WATER, GIVING IT A DRY AND CRUMBLY TEXTURE. IN MY 'DECARBED' VERSION THE EGG DOES NOT GIVE AN EGGY TASTE AT ALL, BUT ADDS GREAT PROTEIN AND NUTRIENTS INSTEAD.

1 egg
2 Tbsp fine desiccated coconut
¾ cup almond flour
2 Tbsp psyllium powder
Pinch salt
2 tsp baking powder
1 Tbsp apple cider vinegar
½ cup boiling water

Crack the egg into a microwavable mixing bowl and whisk briefly with a fork.

In a separate bowl, mix the coconut, almond flour, psyllium, salt and baking powder thoroughly. Layer the mixture on top of the egg in the microwave bowl. Add the vinegar to the boiling water and fold into the rest of the ingredients with a fork, making sure the egg gets worked into the batter without overworking it. Pop into the microwave for 2½–3 minutes on high. It should feel dry and spongy.

Allow to cool for 2 minutes, and then use a fork to gently flake the muffin-like cake into smaller chunks.

Serve as a lovely warm porridge with butter, a sprinkle of xylitol and milk or amasi.

Yields 4 servings at 4 g carbs per serving.

LEKKER TIPS

- See also the 'decarbed' *Pap en Wors met Smoor* (p. 114).

Creamy porridge

THIS IS MY GO-TO BREAKFAST ON A WINTER'S MORNING.

½ cup flaxseed (freshly milled in your coffee grinder)
½ cup pumpkin seeds (freshly milled into flour)
4 Tbsp fine desiccated coconut
2 Tbsp butter
6 Tbsp fresh cream or coconut cream
Boiling water to suit your preferred consistency (¼–⅓ cup per serving)
2 tsp xylitol (optional)

Grind the flaxseed and pumpkin seeds in your coffee grinder to make flour. Divide between two bowls.

Add 2 Tbsp coconut, 1 Tbsp butter and 3 Tbsp cream to each bowl. Now slowly pour boiling water over the porridge while stirring to incorporate the butter and cream until it is the consistency you prefer. Sprinkle over some xylitol if using. The porridge will thicken up quickly and needs to be eaten right away!

Yields 2 very filling and fibre-filled servings at 5 g carbs per serving. It is suitable for children aged nine months and up. Portions must be made smaller for the kids.

Almost instant breakfast cereal

BASIC MIX
3 cups nut flour of your choice
(or 2 cups nut flour and 1 cup
pumpkin seed meal – see How to
make your own nut and seed flour,
pp. 22–24)
2 Tbsp psyllium husks
1½ cups flax meal
1½ cups fine desiccated coconut

Mix all the ingredients together and then divide the mixture between two jars. Add the flavour options of choice:

'Coco' cereal

Mix 2 Tbsp cocoa powder, 1 Tbsp dark chocolate chips (optional) and 2 Tbsp xylitol into the jar.
5.5 g carbs per serving.

Fruity cereal

Add ½ x 44 g container Simply Delish natural jelly (available from Dis-Chem, health stores and some retailers; it comes in four flavours: strawberry, raspberry, orange and peach) to the jar. Store airtight in the refrigerator for 7–10 days. To serve, spoon 3–4 Tbsp cereal into a bowl, add a little hot water and then a healthy fat such as fresh cream or coconut cream.
4 g carbs per serving, excluding the milk or cream.

LEKKER TIPS

- Using natural, sugar-free jelly adds some much-needed excitement to our mornings. Kids love this one!
- Fresh berries or a quarter grated apple and cinnamon will do the trick too.
- Treat it like you would prepare any wheat-based, instant cereal. This will be very filling, but not as much as your morning bacon and eggs, so be sure to pack some protein into the lunchbox.

FABULOUS FLAX!

Flaxseed is the food with the highest amount of lignans (CANCER-FIGHTING ANTIOXIDANTS). It is high in OMEGA-3 and a very good source of FIBRE. It lowers blood pressure, lowers oxidative stress in the blood vessels and IMPROVES METABOLIC SYNDROME. Flax has strong ANTI-INFLAMMATORY properties and it improves intestinal absorption of nutrients. It also improves acne and ADHD, regulates blood sugar and BOOSTS MEMORY!

Blueberry muffins

½ cup milled flaxseed
½ cup fine desiccated coconut
1 cup nut flour (almond or pecan)
2 tsp baking powder
Pinch salt
½ cup amasi, full-cream milk or coconut milk
2 eggs
⅓ cup butter, melted
2 Tbsp xylitol
¾ cup fresh or frozen blueberries

Preheat the oven to 180 °C. Line 10 of the holes of a 12-hole muffin tray with muffin cups.

Mix the flaxseed, coconut, flour, baking powder and salt together in one bowl. In another bowl, cream the amasi, eggs, melted butter and xylitol together. Add the wet ingredients to the dry ingredients and mix well to make a batter.

Lightly mix the berries into the batter. Scoop the batter into the muffin cups and bake for 15–20 minutes until the muffins are brown and spongy.

Yields 10 muffins at about 4.5 g carbs per muffin.

LEKKER TIPS

- These muffins can be frozen for handy lunchbox snacks.
- Use any berries or mix grated apple into the batter with a sprinkle of cinnamon. Scoop Berry Jam (p. 136) into the centre of the batter in the muffin cup for a nice little surprise!

Savoury muffins

3 large eggs
⅓ cup amasi, full-cream milk, plain double-cream yoghurt or coconut milk
⅓ cup melted butter
1½ cups almond flour
½ cup coconut meal
2 tsp baking powder
½ cup chopped smoked chicken
½ cup crumbled feta cheese
2 sprigs fresh thyme, leaves only
1 tsp crushed garlic
1 cup finely chopped spinach

Preheat the oven to 180 °C. Line 10 of the holes of a small 12-hole muffin tray with muffin cups.

Beat the eggs and amasi into the melted butter.

In a separate bowl, mix the almond flour, coconut meal and baking powder together. Add the chicken, cheese, thyme, garlic and spinach and mix well into the dry ingredients.

Now add the egg mix to the dry mix. Mix but do not overwork the batter.

Divide the batter evenly between the muffin cups and bake for 15–20 minutes. The muffins should be brown and set on top.

Yields 10 muffins at 3 g carbs per muffin.

LEKKER TIPS

- Make variations to your hearts content: swap the feta for ½ cup grated Cheddar, mozzarella or crumbled blue cheese; swap the chicken for bacon or salami strips; swap the spinach for a handful of fresh basil leaves or a grated baby marrow...

Five-minute toasted breakfast buns

4 Tbsp milled pecan, pumpkin, almond, flaxseed or sunflower seed flour (whatever you have on hand)
4 Tbsp coconut meal
2 Tbsp coconut oil, melted
1 tsp baking powder
1 egg
Sesame seeds to sprinkle (optional)

Mix all the ingredients, except the sesame seeds, together in a small ramekin (more or less the circumference of a regular hamburger bun). Sprinkle with sesame seeds if using. Microwave on high for 60–80 seconds. It is ready when it starts to pull away from the sides but still feels nice and spongy. Pop it out of the ramekin, cut in half and toast in a pan with a knob of butter.

Serve one or two halves topped with one of many filling options. Here are a few ideas to get you going:
- Salami strips, scrambled egg and cheese
- Beef mince, herbed mushroom slices and cheese
- Egg, sautéed spinach leaves, pan-fried tomatoes and melted mozzarella cheese

Serve 1 whole bun or 2 halves at about 6 g carbs per bun.

LEKKER TIPS

- You can bake a larger batch in the oven if you quadruple the recipe and bake it in a preheated oven at 180 °C for 15–20 minutes.

Breakfast pizza

6 eggs
About ½ x 230 g block cream cheese
2 Tbsp coconut oil
Tomato Sauce (p. 136) or tomato purée
1 cup meat of your choice (salami, bacon bits, smoked chicken, roast chicken, bolognaise mince, Parma ham)
½ avocado, sliced
1 cup grated Cheddar or mozzarella cheese

Preheat the oven grill.

In a food processor, mix the eggs and the cream cheese together until all the cream cheese clumps are dissolved.

Heat the coconut oil in a large ovenproof frying pan on medium heat. Pour all the egg mixture into the pan and allow to set for 3–4 minutes with the lid on. The sides should just start to set.

Quickly pop the pan under the grill and allow the top half to set as well. As soon as the top half is firm enough, take out of the oven and add the tomato sauce, toppings and cheese. Pop back under the grill until the cheese has melted.

Yields 3–4 servings at about 4 g carbs per serving.

LEKKER TIPS

- These slices are awesome for lunchboxes.
- Serve them cold on your stoep in summer with a stack of rocket and fresh chopped tomatoes drizzled with flavoured olive oil.

Breakfast wraps

6 eggs
Pinch salt
About ½ x 230 g block cream cheese
⅓ cup fine desiccated coconut
Coconut oil to fry

Using a food processor, mix the eggs, salt and cream cheese together until all the cream cheese clumps are dissolved. Give the desiccated coconut a quick whizz in the grinder and add to the egg mix.

Melt some coconut oil in a pan on high heat and pour in enough batter to cover the base of the pan. You want the batter to be only a few millimetres thick (basically, the thickness of a pancake or tortilla).

As soon as the batter has settled and you can easily insert a spatula under the wrap, lift up a corner to see if it has browned enough and then flip. Remove from the pan and keep warm while you make the rest. To serve, add a filling of your choice, roll up and enjoy!

Yields 6–8 wraps at about 2 g carbs per wrap.

Filling suggestions
Smoor (p. 114), boerewors wheels and cheese
Chicken, Cherry Tomato and Ginger Jam (p. 136) and feta cheese

LEKKER TIPS

- These wraps are versatile and filling. They are wonderful if you stuff them, allow them to cool down and then pack them into a lunchbox.
- This is a smart way of using leftover bolognaise or chicken and is a great way to incorporate stir-fried veggies.

Easy veggie seed crackers

Finger Foods

Easy veggie seed crackers

½ cup ground almonds
½ cup flax meal
½ cup mixed sunflower, flax, sesame and pumpkin seeds
2 Tbsp poppy seeds (optional)
3 Tbsp grated Parmesan cheese or
1 cup grated Cheddar cheese
1 large baby marrow, finely grated
A sprinkle of your favourite mixed herbs or spices
4 Tbsp boiling water
1 free-range egg
1 tsp psyllium husks

Preheat the oven to 180 °C. Butter a baking tray.

Mix all the ingredients together and roll out thinly on the prepared baking tray. Mark into squares.

Bake for 20–25 minutes until brown and crispy. Allow to cool in the switched-off oven.

Break into pieces and serve. Store what you don't use in an airtight container.

Yields a platter for 6–8 guests at about 15 g carbs for the entire tray.

Fried Camembert mushroom with tomato ginger jam

2 Tbsp coconut oil
1 large brown mushroom
Salt and Pepper
1 whole Camembert cheese
3 Tbsp Cherry Tomato and Ginger Jam (p. 136)

Heat 1 Tbsp coconut oil in a frying pan on medium heat and fry the mushroom on both sides until tender and cooked through. Season with salt and pepper (or even a bit of your favourite herb blend). Place it onto a serving platter.

In the same warm pan, add the remaining tablespoon of coconut oil and gently fry the cheese on one side for 1 minute. Turn over and fry the other side. The cheese must stay intact but still be browned nicely. Place the cheese on top of the mushroom – it should fit snugly inside the mushroom. Scoop the tomato jam into the pan and heat slightly on low heat. Drizzle the warmed jam over the fried cheese and mushroom.

Yields 4 servings at about 2 g carbs per serving.

LEKKER TIPS

- Serve with fresh Low-Carb Bread (pp. 147–148) or Easy Veggie Seed Crackers (above).
- You can omit the mushroom if you want to serve up a more dainty cheese platter. This recipe makes for a robust, rustic platter that can be accompanied by pan-roasted pepper halves, olives, thinly sliced steak strips and guacamole.

Homemade cheese ball

4 cups amasi

Line a sieve or colander with muslin or cheesecloth and place over a sturdy bowl to catch the whey. Pour the amasi into the sieve. Pull up the sides of the cloth and tie a string around the ball-shaped, amasi-filled cloth. The whey water will immediately start to drip out. Now hang the cloth by the string in a cool, dry place, such as over a sink (in winter) or in the refrigerator (in summer). Allow to drip for 16–24 hours.

Gently open the cloth and take out the beautiful cheese ball. Now divide the cheese ball into five smaller balls. Wrap separately in plastic wrap and refrigerate until you are ready to add some toppings (see below) and serve them on a beautiful platter!

Yields 5 small cheese balls at 3–4 g carbs per cheese ball. (Perfect for a snack platter serving 8–10 guests.)

Fig-stuffed cheese ball with pecan-caramel sauce

2 small Homemade Cheese Balls (see above)
1 ripe fresh fig, roughly chopped

PECAN-CARAMEL SAUCE
4 Tbsp butter
1 Tbsp xylitol
2 Tbsp fresh cream
¼ cup pecan nuts, roughly chopped

For the cheese balls, use a plastic-lined small ramekin or mug and, flatten 1 cheese ball. Layer the chopped fig on top of the flattened cheese ball.

Place the second cheese ball on top of the fig layer and flatten slightly. Now wrap plastic around the cheese to form it into the shape of a ball again and pop into the refrigerator while you make the pecan topping.

For the sauce, melt the butter in a small saucepan over medium heat. Add the xylitol and allow to dissolve while stirring a bit. Add the cream and allow to bubble and thicken for a minute. Lastly add the chopped pecans, turn the heat to low, and allow to thicken and brown for a minute. Remove from heat and allow to cool.

Place the fig-filled cheese ball on a serving platter and smother with the pecan sauce.

Yields 10 servings at 1.8 g carbs per serving.

Mini cheese ball trio

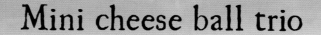

3 Homemade Cheese Balls
(see opposite)

GARLIC AND HERB
1 tsp chopped garlic
1 tsp chilli flakes
1 tsp chopped fresh herbs (chives,
thyme or parsley)
1 tsp olive oil
Salt and pepper

BLACK PEPPER AND LEMON ZEST
Finely grated zest of ½ lemon
1 tsp ground black pepper
1 Tbsp olive oil
1 Tbsp lemon juice

PESTO DRIZZLE
1 Tbsp olive oil
1 Tbsp pesto of your choice

For the garlic and herb, mix all the ingredients together and scoop onto a plate or cutting board. Roll 1 cheese ball in the mix until it is evenly coated. Place onto a serving platter.

For the black pepper and lemon zest, mix the lemon zest and pepper together and scoop onto a plate or cutting board. Roll 1 cheese ball in the mix until it is evenly coated. Place onto the serving platter and drizzle with the olive oil and lemon juice.

For the pesto drizzle, mix the olive oil and pesto to a runny consistency. Place the last cheese ball onto the serving platter and drizzle over the pesto mixture.

Yields a platter for 6–8 guests at about 4 g carbs per ball or 2 g carbs per serving for 6 servings.

Snack-e-licious spicy seed crunch

Snack-e-licious sweet seed crunch

4 Tbsp roughly chopped nuts (any
nuts except cashews or peanuts)
¼ cup pumpkin seeds
8 Tbsp sunflower seeds
1 cup coconut flakes
1 Tbsp xylitol
½ tsp ground cinnamon

Toast the nuts, seeds and coconut flakes together in a dry pan on medium heat. Stir often. As soon as the coconut flakes start to brown, add the xylitol and cinnamon. When the xylitol melts, stir this syrup into the seed mixture until everything is covered and glossy. Allow to caramelise slightly and then tip into a serving bowl.

Yields a snack bowl suited for 4–6 guests at about 3.4 g carbs each.

Snack-e-licious spicy seed crunch

4 Tbsp roughly chopped nuts (any
nuts except cashews or peanuts)
4 Tbsp pumpkin seeds
8 Tbsp sunflower seeds
1 cup coconut flakes
¼ tsp turmeric
¼ tsp ground cinnamon
¼ tsp ground cumin
¼ tsp salt
¼ tsp mild curry powder or
chilli flakes
Knob of coconut oil

Toast the nuts, seeds and coconut flakes together in a dry pan on medium heat. Stir often. As soon as the coconut flakes start to brown, add all the spices and coconut oil. Allow the spices to infuse all the seeds and then remove from heat.

Yields a snack bowl suited for 4–6 guests at about 3 g carbs each.

Feta and fruit mini kebabs

ADD CONTRASTING FRESH BURSTS TO YOUR PLATTERS BY COMBINING LOW-CARB FRUIT AND FETA CUBES ON TOOTHPICKS. THESE BITE-SIZE PIECES INCORPORATE SMALL AMOUNTS OF FRUIT FOR A WELL-BALANCED, NUTRITIOUS SPREAD WITHOUT THE SUGAR SPIKE.

Feta cheese, cubed
AND
1 prickly pear, cubed
(100 g feta, cubed + 1 fruit, cubed =
10 g carbs)
OR
10 strawberries, halved
(100 g feta, cubed + 1 fruit, halved
= 9 g carbs)
OR
20 fresh blueberries or raspberries
(100 g feta, cubed + 1 fruit = 8–9 g
carbs)
OR
⅛ melon, cubed or balled
(100 g feta, cubed + 1 fruit, cubed =
9 g carbs)

Thread 1 cheese cube and 1 fruit cube of your choice onto a toothpick. Repeat until you have filled a platter with mini kebabs.

Pumpkin 'hummus'

1 cup cooked and drained pumpkin
1 cup pumpkin seed meal
1 Tbsp olive oil
¼ tsp ground cinnamon
¼ tsp ground cumin
½ tsp crushed garlic
Splash of lemon juice
Salt and black pepper to taste
Chopped fresh coriander, parsley
or rosemary leaves to garnish

Using a stick blender, blend all the ingredients except the garnish. Spoon into a bowl, garnish and refrigerate.

Serve with Rustic Bread (p. 148) or Easy Veggie Seed Crackers (p. 47), roasted or fresh veggie spears and Mini Meatballs (p. 56). Use toothpicks to dip the meatballs into the hummus.

Yields a bowl to serve a party of 8–10 guests at 2–3 g carbs per serving.

Chicken wings two ways

1 kg chicken wings (or more if the cousins and their cousins are coming around)
4 Tbsp olive oil
1 quantity Fragrant Basting Sauce (p. 140)
½ cup Tomato Sauce (p. 136)
Barbecue spice of your choice

Parboil the chicken wings in a saucepan of salted water for about 20 minutes. Preheat the oven to 200 °C.

Drain the chicken wings and remove the wing tips. (You can use them to make stock by adding them back into the precook water.) Cut the rest of the wings at the joint and divide your smaller portioned wings between two bowls.

Bowl 1: Pour 2 Tbsp of the olive oil and some fragrant basting sauce over the wings and toss to coat with the mixture.
Bowl 2: Pour the rest of the olive, the tomato sauce and a good sprinkle of barbecue spice over the wings and toss until well coated with the mixture.

Place the wings in two separate ovenproof dishes and bake them for about 5 minutes on each side. Set your oven to grill to give the wings some char treatment. Serve with veggie sticks and a whipped sour cream or a peri-peri mayonnaise dip.

Each of the two bowls will add an amount of 8 g carbs, which can be divided by the number of chicken wings yielded from each bowl.

Mini quiche

Chicken and cheese cupcakes with creamy cheese 'icing'

CUPCAKES
500 g chicken mince
1 tsp salt and pepper to taste
2 tsp dried mixed herbs
1 cup grated cheese of choice
1 free-range egg
2 Tbsp fine desiccated coconut
2 tsp crushed garlic

CREAMY CHEESE 'ICING'
½ x 230 g block cream cheese
2 Tbsp butter, at room temperature
1 Tbsp lemon juice
4 Tbsp grated cheese of choice
Chopped fresh chives to sprinkle
Black pepper or paprika (optional)

Preheat the oven to 180 °C. Set out a 12-hole silicon muffin tray or butter a metal muffin tray.

For the cupcakes, mix all the ingredients together in a bowl. Scoop the mixture into 8–10 of the muffin tray holes, filling them to two-thirds full. Bake for 20–25 minutes or until the chicken has set into a dense, solid cupcake. Allow to cool while you make the 'icing'.

For the icing, use a stick blender and blend all the ingredients together. Scoop into a piping bag and swirl onto the cooled chicken cupcakes. Sprinkle with chives and add a grinding of pepper or dusting of paprika if desired. Refrigerate and serve with a salad.

Yields 8–10 cupcakes at about 2 g carbs per cupcake.

Mini quiche

CRUST
4 Tbsp ground almonds or pumpkin seeds
½ cup ground flaxseed
½ cup mixed seeds
2 Tbsp grated Parmesan or Cheddar
1 baby marrow, finely grated
4 tsp butter

FILLING
3 free-range eggs
4 Tbsp fresh cream
1 small handful chopped rocket or baby spinach leaves
1 large handful grated mozzarella
5 slices salami, chopped
3 cherry tomatoes, halved
Salt and pepper to taste

Preheat the oven to 180 °C. Set out a 6-hole muffin tray.

For the crust, place all the ingredients, except the butter, into a bowl and mix together. Rub the butter through the mixture. Press the crust into the base and up the sides of the muffin holes. Bake for 5–7 minutes. Remove from the oven (leave it switched on) and set aside, still in the tray.

For the filling, mix all the ingredients together in a bowl and scoop into the crust bases. Bake at 180 °C for about 15 minutes until the quiches are puffy and set.

Yields 6 mini quiches at about 4 g carbs per quiche.

Mini meatballs

MEATBALLS ARE WONDERFUL ANY TIME AND A REAL HIT IN A LUNCHBOX. BUT IF YOU DRESS THESE MINI MINIONS NICELY, THEY CAN BE THE STAR OF MANY A LONG, LAZY SUMMER 'STOEP VISIT'. HERE ARE A FEW MEATBALL RECIPES WITH A TWIST THAT WILL ADD SOME SERIOUS PIZZAZZ!

MOROCCAN MEATBALLS
500 g lamb mince
1 handful finely chopped fresh coriander
Grated zest and juice of ½ lemon
1½ tsp Moroccan Spice (p. 135)
½ tsp salt
2 tsp crushed garlic
2 Tbsp coconut oil

Mix all the ingredients together, except the coconut oil. Roll the meat mixture into about 20 mini balls.

Heat the coconut oil in a pan on medium to high heat and fry the meatballs on all sides until nicely browned.

Serve hot or cold in a bowl with toothpicks on the side, or make Mini Moroccan Kebabs by threading a meatball, a cube of feta and an olive onto a toothpick.

Yields about 20 mini meatballs at 0.5 g carbs per meatball.

BOBOTIE MEATBALLS
500 g beef mince (not lean)
3 Tbsp fine desiccated coconut
1 free-range egg
2 Tbsp xylitol
1 Tbsp medium curry powder
1 tsp turmeric
¼ cup full-cream milk
1 small onion, finely chopped
Salt and pepper
2 Tbsp coconut oil

Mix all the ingredients together, except the coconut oil. Roll the meat mixture into about 20 mini balls.

Heat the coconut oil in a pan on medium to high heat and fry the meatballs on all sides until nicely browned.

Serve hot or cold in a bowl with toothpicks on the side, and a bowl of Old-fashioned Sweet Mustard Sauce (p. 142) as a dip.

Yields about 20 meatballs at about 1 g carbs per meatball.

TANGY BBQ PORK MEATBALLS
500 g pork mince
1 baby marrow, grated
2 Tbsp red pepper, finely chopped (optional)
1 Tbsp barbecue spice of your choice (without sugar)
1 free-range egg
1 tsp Dijon mustard
1 Tbsp xylitol
3 Tbsp fine desiccated coconut
2 Tbsp coconut oil

Mix all the ingredients together, except the coconut oil. Roll the meat mixture into about 20 mini balls.

Heat the coconut oil in a pan on medium to high heat and fry the meatballs on all sides until nicely browned.

Serve hot or cold in a bowl with toothpicks on the side, and a bowl of Old-fashioned Sweet Mustard Sauce (p. 142) as a dip.

Yields about 20 meatballs at 0.6 g carbs per meatball.

LEKKER TIPS

- All these meatball mixes can also be spread out and baked on a baking tray. Bake at 180 °C for 15–20 minutes. Cut into four equal strips and use the Creamy Cheese Icing (p. 55) as a filling between strips. Cut into triangles to make the cutest little meat sandwiches.

Mediterranean meatloaf

MEATLOAF
500 g chicken mince
1 cup cooked and mashed pumpkin
1 handful chopped fresh parsley
2 free-range eggs
½ cup fine desiccated coconut
½ cup grated Cheddar cheese
¼ cup fresh cream
½ tsp salt
¼ tsp pepper
2 tsp dried mixed herbs
1 tsp crushed garlic

ROAST VEGGIES
6–8 tomatoes on the vine
6 medium baby marrows, shaved lengthways into ribbons
1 brinjal, thinly sliced and dégorged (drained of excess juices)
2 Tbsp melted coconut oil
Herbed salt and black pepper to sprinkle

TO SERVE
8–10 rashers bacon, grilled or fried until crisp
Olive oil to drizzle
Whipped sour cream and chopped chives

Preheat the oven to 180 °C. Set aside a silicone loaf pan or butter a metal loaf pan.

For the meatloaf, place all the ingredients into a bowl and mix well. Transfer the mixture into the loaf pan and bake for 40–50 minutes.

For the roast veggies, place them on a baking tray and drizzle with coconut oil. Bake alongside the meatloaf for 25–30 minutes. Turn every 6–8 minutes until the veggies are cooked through and start to caramelise ever so slightly.

Sprinkle the veggies with herbed salt and pepper.

To serve, turn out the chicken meatloaf into the centre of the serving platter and arrange the brinjal slices around the platter. Stack the marrow ribbons and crispy bacon rashers on top of the meatloaf and place the roast tomatoes on top of the marrows or on the side of the platter. Drizzle with olive oil and add a small bowl of whipped sour cream with chopped chives for guests to drizzle over the brinjal.

Yields 4–6 servings at 13 g carbs per serving.

Curried green bean salad

JUST LIKE GRANDMA'S.

500 g fresh green beans
1 Tbsp coconut oil
1 medium to large onion, chopped
⅔ cup white vinegar
5 Tbsp xylitol
2 tsp mild curry powder
1½ tsp turmeric
1 tsp salt
½ tsp psyllium husks

Slice the green beans finely, crossways.

Heat the coconut oil in a saucepan on medium heat and sauté the onion until translucent. Add the green beans and sauté until they start to soften.

Add the vinegar, xylitol, curry powder, turmeric and salt to the beans and allow to simmer for 5–8 minutes. Top up with a little water at a time if the sauce reduces too quickly. Once the sauce has thickened slightly, remove from heat and stir in the psyllium for 1 minute.

Transfer the bean salad into a glass jar with a lid, allow to cool down and then refrigerate. Serve chilled with salami or roast beef, cheese and crackers.

Yields 6–8 servings. (Three heaped tablespoons should be seen as a 4–5 g carbs serving, so it helps to scoop a teaspoon at a time onto a cracker with cheese as a topping.)

Five-minute asparagus salad

FOR THOSE CRAZY KIND OF DAYS …

SALAD
1 x 410 g can asparagus salad cuts
1 x 410 g can green beans
1 avocado, cubed
1 small onion, chopped
8 cherry tomatoes, halved
Black olives, halved (optional)

DRESSING
4 Tbsp olive oil
4 Tbsp apple cider vinegar
Salt and pepper
1 tsp crushed garlic
1 tsp xylitol

Open, chop, mix, assemble and pour. That's it!

Yields 4 servings at about 6.5 g carbs per serving.

Curried green bean salad

Warm spinach salad

2 Tbsp butter
1 x 300 g packet baby spinach
½ chorizo sausage, sliced
6 sun-dried tomatoes, chopped
1 x 125 g punnet sugar snap peas
2 smoked chicken breasts, cubed
1 wheel feta cheese
1 orange or red pepper, chopped
1 avocado, cubed
2 Spring onions, Chopped
1 quantity Poppy, Lime and Ginger
Dressing (p. 144)

Melt the butter in a large saucepan or frying pan and sauté the spinach until just wilted. Place the warm spinach in a serving dish. Sauté the chorizo and sun-dried tomato in the same pan on medium heat for about 1 minute. Stack the other salad ingredients on top of the warm spinach and finally top with the warm chorizo and sun-dried tomatoes. Serve with the dressing on the side.

Yields 4–6 side servings at 5 g carbs per serving or 2 main servings at about 14 g per serving.

Bacon, broccoli and red cabbage salad

½ head broccoli, finely chopped in a food processor
¼ head red cabbage, finely shredded in a food processor
¼ head green cabbage, finely shredded in a food processor
1 cup grated Cheddar cheese
1 x 250 g packet bacon bits
½ cup sunflower seeds
2 tsp xylitol
1 cup Creamy Mayo (p. 139)
2 Tbsp apple cider vinegar

Mix the chopped veggies and grated cheese together in a bowl.

Fry the bacon bits until crispy. Pour the bacon along with the pan juices over the veggie mixture and toss through.

Toast the sunflower seeds in a dry pan with 1 tsp of the xylitol. Sprinkle on top of the salad.

Mix the mayo, vinegar and remaining xylitol together and mix into the slaw.

Yields 4–6 side servings at 5 g carbs per serving.

Black Forest salad

1 x 230 g block cream cheese
Grated zest of 1 orange
1 x 50 g packet slivered almonds
1 x 120 g packet baby green leaf mix
1 avocado, sliced
18 whole blackberries
⅓ cucumber, sliced and quartered
12 slices Black Forest ham, halved
10–12 grape-size cream cheese balls rolled in orange zest
1 quantity Blackberry Vinaigrette (p. 144)

Cut 10–12 cubes out of the cream cheese block, roll into small cheese balls and coat with the orange zest.

Toast the slivered almonds in a dry pan.

Assemble the salad and drizzle individual portions with the vinaigrette. Allow your heart to yodel while you eat.

Yields 4–6 side servings at about 4.5 g carbs per serving.

Soup

Basic bone broth

WHILE MANY OF US TEND TO SEE BONES AS SOMETHING CLOSE TO DOG FOOD, CHEFS KNOW JUST HOW MUCH TASTE AND GOODNESS IS LOCKED UP IN THE GELATINE-FILLED BONES AND CONNECTIVE TISSUE OF AN ANIMAL. IN ADDITION, MANY A DEGENERATIVE AND INFLAMMATORY DISEASE CAN BE CORRECTED BY INTRODUCING MORE GELATINE INTO THE DIET. GET A SYSTEM IN PLACE TO ALWAYS HAVE AT LEAST THREE CONTAINERS OF BONE BROTH READY IN YOUR FREEZER. SIMPLY USE MEAT OFFCUTS, BONES AND TRIMMINGS, AND BOIL THE 'LIVING GELATIN' OUT OF THEM ALONG WITH SOME CELERY LEAVES, GARLIC, ONION, A CARROT AND A SQUEEZE OF LEMON JUICE OR APPLE CIDER VINEGAR.

About 1 kg bones (use any of these bones: grass-fed marrowbones, beef, lamb, free-range poultry, pork, fish, chicken wings, necks or feet, and don't frown upon trotters, you can use them too!)
3 Tbsp lemon juice or apple cider vinegar
1 large onion, quartered
2 medium carrots, roughly chopped
2 Tbsp chopped garlic
½ bunch celery (ribs and leaves), roughly chopped
1 small bunch fresh parsley, chopped
Salt to taste
5 black peppercorns

Add the bones and lemon juice to a big stockpot or slow-cooker and cover with boiling water (you want to keep the bones covered in water, so top up as necessary with boiling water). Allow to stand for 20 minutes and then add the rest of the ingredients.

If using the stovetop, bring to a rapid boil and then turn the heat down to the lowest possible setting and simmer for at least 3 hours, but to get most of the benefits simmer for 8 hours or longer. This is where a slow-cooker comes in very handy. Just set on low and cook through the night, making sure to top up the water just before you go to bed.

Skim any impurities you see on the surface at any time during the cooking process. If you have the luxury of cooking your broth for a very long time, you can strain it as soon as the bones crumble when pressed. Chicken and fish bone broth will achieve this stage within 6–8 hours.

Strain the broth and discard all the bones and veggies. Cool and store in the refrigerator for 5 days or freeze for a few months.

Yields 8–10 cups at 2 g carbs per cup.

LEKKER TIPS

- If you really want to invest in your health, start by investing in a slow-cooker and look at bones as mineral powerhouses instead of dog treats. A cup of broth a day will not only keep the doctor away, it will also give the pharmacist less pay!

Hearty marrowbone and veggie soup

8 marrowbones with a tiny bit of
meat on the bone
2 tsp herbed salt (I use garlic and
parsley salt)
2 tsp black pepper
4 celery sticks, chopped
1 brinjal, chopped
1 leek, chopped
1 red pepper, chopped
1 medium onion, chopped
½ x 400 g packet or 1½ cups cubed
pumpkin
Coconut oil or lard for frying
1 tsp paprika
½ tsp cumin
2 bay leaves
1 tsp turmeric
1 tsp thyme
1 tsp ground coriander
10–11 cups water
4 Tbsp apple cider vinegar
2 Tbsp xylitol
2 Tbsp crushed garlic
1 handful fresh parsley, chopped
1 x 115 g can tomato paste
Sprigs fresh coriander to garnish

Preheat the oven to 200 °C.

Spread the marrowbones on a baking tray, sprinkle liberally with salt and pepper and bake for 20 minutes. The marrow should start to bubble slightly but not melt.

While the bones are in the oven, stir-fry all the chopped veggies in coconut oil or lard. Add the spices and 6 cups of the water. Allow to simmer.

As soon as the bones are browned and ready, add them to the veggies and simmer until the liquid is reduced by almost half. Add the vinegar, xylitol, garlic, parsley and tomato paste. Top up with another 4–5 cups water and simmer for 30–40 minutes. Top up liquid if needed, but this is meant to be a hearty, thick soup.

Serve each portion with a marrowbone and garnish with sprigs of fresh coriander.

Yields 4–6 servings (4 servings = 14 g carbs per serving, 6 servings = 9.5 g carbs per serving).

LEKKER TIPS

- You can make this soup in a slow-cooker too and have the heartiness meet your nose at the door the moment you come home.
- Bone marrow is an excellent brain food. You can even roast the bones a bit longer and enjoy the marrow goodness on its own.

Cream of leek and cauliflower soup with salami strips

2 Tbsp coconut oil or butter
3 leeks, chopped
3 thick pork rashers, cubed
1 tsp herbed salt
Grind of pepper to taste
1 Tbsp chopped garlic (less if you use bone broth)
1 large head cauliflower, broken into florets
7–8 cups water or broth
1 cup fresh cream
¼ x 230 g block cream cheese
1 bunch fresh chives, chopped
Grated Cheddar cheese and strips of salami to garnish

Heat the coconut oil in a saucepan on medium heat and sauté the chopped leeks and cubed pork rashers until the leeks are soft and slightly caramelised.

Add the salt, pepper, garlic, cauliflower florets and half of the water. Let the liquid reduce and cook the cauliflower florets until soft. Add the cream and cream cheese and allow to simmer for 5–10 minutes.

Remove from heat and purée with a stick blender or in a regular blender. Add the rest of the water and chopped chives. Return to the heat and simmer and reduce to your preferred consistency. Garnish and serve.

Yields 4 servings at 11 g carbs per serving.

Chicken noodle soup

Chicken noodle soup

SHIRATAKI NOODLES (AT HEALTH STORES) ARE MADE FROM AN ASIAN ROOT AND HAVE ZERO CARBS. ALTHOUGH A BIT PRICEY, IT MAKES ALL THE DIFFERENCE TO THIS SOUP, AND THE KIDS WILL LOVE IT!

1 kg free-range chicken pieces, skin on
8 cups water
1 bunch table celery leaves and stalks, chopped
2 medium onions or 4 spring onions, chopped
Garlic to taste
2 tsp fresh thyme leaves or ½ tsp mixed dried herbs
2 small carrots, halved
Salt and pepper to taste
1 cup fresh cream or coconut milk (optional)
1 x 320 g packet shirataki noodles

If you start from scratch with raw chicken pieces, brown them first in a little coconut oil in a large heavy-bottomed saucepan on medium heat. Add salt and pepper.

Add the water, celery, onions, garlic, thyme and carrots. Cook until the meat falls off the bones, adding more water when needed to maintain the consistency you prefer. (Simmer on medium heat with the bones for as long as possible.)

Discard the bones and season to taste before stirring in the cream and shirataki noodles. Allow to heat through for a minute and then serve.

Yields 6–8 servings (6 servings = 6 g carbs per serving, 8 servings = 4 g carbs per serving).

LEKKER TIPS

- If you cannot find the shirataki noodles, don't stress. This soup is delicious without it too.

Creamy cauli, spinach and mushroom soup

3 Tbsp butter
2 x 250 g punnets of your favourite mushrooms, sliced
3 red spring onions, chopped
1 large head cauliflower, chopped
3 cups chicken stock
3 cups water
Garlic to taste
1¾ cups fresh cream
Salt and pepper to taste
½ tsp dried mixed herbs (optional)
1 x 200 g packet baby spinach
Chopped fresh chives to garnish

Heat the butter in a saucepan on medium heat and sauté the mushrooms, spring onions and cauliflower until soft. (Set aside some mushrooms for garnishing.) Add the stock, water, garlic, 1½ cups cream, seasoning and herbs and allow to simmer on low heat for 15–20 minutes. Add the spinach 5 minutes before removing from heat.

Remove from heat and blend using a stick blender or ordinary blender. Return to the stovetop and simmer for another 10 minutes on very low heat. Add a bit more stock or water to top up to your preferred consistency. Garnish with a swirl of cream, some chives and a pretty little sautéed mushroom.

Yields 4 servings at 8 g carbs per serving.

German *kohl* soup

2 Tbsp butter or coconut oil
1 onion, chopped
3 celery sticks, chopped
1 Tbsp crushed garlic
½ tsp caraway seeds
600 g pork shoulder chops
Herbed salt and pepper to taste
(I use garlic and parsley salt)
16 cups water
1 medium cabbage, chopped
6 cauliflower florets
6–8 mange tout, chopped
2 tsp barbecue spice
¼ green pepper, chopped
¼ red pepper, chopped

Heat the butter or coconut oil in a large saucepan on medium heat and sauté the onion, celery, garlic and caraway seeds.

Cut 1 pork chop in half and add it to the onion mix along with the seasoning. Sauté until the pork has browned some. Add the water and allow to boil for 20–30 minutes to form a broth. Add the cabbage, and boil for another 20 minutes or until the meat and cabbage is soft.

Take the meat out, chop it into cubes and set aside. Add the cauliflower and mange tout to the saucepan, and some more water and spices if needed.

Heat some coconut oil in a frying pan. Spice the remaining chops with the barbecue spice and pan fry until browned on one side. After you have turned the chops for the first time, add the chopped peppers and sauté while you finish cooking the meat. Once done, allow the meat to rest and then cut into cubes. Spoon the soup into bowls and then add the meat into the steaming soup.

Yields 4–6 filling servings (4 servings = 9 g carbs per serving, 6 servings = 6 g carbs per serving).

Coconut, butternut and chicken soup

CHICKEN BROTH
2 Tbsp coconut oil
6–8 free-range chicken pieces, skin on
Salt and pepper to taste
1 tsp crushed garlic
3 celery sticks
2 baby carrots
1 medium onion
½ x 400 packet or 1½ cups cubed butternut
6 baby marrows, grated
10 cups water

SPICE MIX
½ tsp ground ginger
1½ tsp turmeric
½ tsp ground cinnamon
1 x 400 ml can coconut milk
Toasted coconut flakes to garnish

For the broth, heat the coconut oil in a saucepan on medium heat and brown the chicken pieces. Add the salt, pepper and garlic.

Add all the remaining broth ingredients and simmer for 30–40 minutes until the chicken is soft enough to remove from the bone. Discard all the bones, chop the meat finely and return it to the broth.

Now add all the spices and coconut milk and simmer the soup for another 10–15 minutes. Top up the liquid with water if needed.

Blend the soup to the texture you prefer using a stick blender. Garnish with toasted coconut flakes.

Yields 4–6 servings (4 servings = 17 g carbs per serving, 6 servings = 11.5 g carbs per serving).

Coconut, butternut and chicken soup

ITALIANO

Sweet Italian mini meatball soup

IT'S LIKE SPAGHETTI BOLOGNAISE WITHOUT THE PASTA BUT WITH THE SAME FLAVOUR PALETTE! BAKE A LOVELY LOW-CARB BREAD TO GO WITH THIS MEAL AND 'MAMMA MIAS' WILL ECHO AROUND YOUR TABLE!

2 Tbsp grated Parmesan cheese (optional)

2½ tsp dried mixed herbs (Italian herbs)

500 g good quality beef mince

4 Tbsp coconut oil or lard

1 x 410 g can tomato purée

Salt and pepper to taste (I use garlic and celery flavoured salt)

1 Tbsp crushed garlic

1 tsp dried thyme

2 Tbsp xylitol or a few stevia drops

2–3 cups water or Bone Broth (p. 65)

1 medium brinjal, diced

5 medium baby marrows, diced

6 baby plum tomatoes, diced

1 onion, diced or 3 spring onions, chopped

1 green pepper, diced

Grated mozzarella cheese and chopped fresh chives or parsley to garnish

Mix the Parmesan cheese and ½ tsp of the mixed herbs into the mince and roll it into prune-size meatballs.

Heat 2 Tbsp of the coconut oil in a large, heavy-bottomed saucepan and fry the meatballs until browned on all sides. Add the tomato purée, salt and pepper, garlic, thyme and xylitol. Let it simmer on medium heat for 7–10 minutes and then add 1½ cups of the water.

Preheat the oven grill. Place the brinjal, baby marrows, tomatoes, onion and green pepper on a baking tray with the remaining coconut oil. Char-grill the veggies, stirring once or twice to get more char on the sides.

Place the char-grilled veggies in a blender or food processor with another ½ cup of the water. Give the mix a quick blitz, leaving a third in bigger chunks if you like a chunky, rustic soup. Purée if you like a smooth soup.

Add the veggie mixture to the tomato and meatballs and simmer gently for about 10 minutes, adding another cup of water if needed.

Garnish with grated mozzarella and chopped chives or parsley.

Yields 4 servings at 14 g carbs per serving.

Biltong and pumpkin soup

STOCK
3 beef bones
1 slice onion
1 Tbsp barbecue spice
2 Tbsp ground coriander
1 tsp crushed garlic
1 sprig fresh thyme
1 Tbsp lemon juice
Sprinkle of nutmeg
6 cups water

SOUP
1 x 400 g packet cubed pumpkin or
butternut (pumpkin has less carbs
than butternut)
1 cup fresh cream
1 cup sliced biltong

Combine all the stock ingredients in a saucepan and simmer for about 30 minutes.

Remove the bones and thyme from the stock. Add the pumpkin to the stock and simmer until soft. Top up with a bit of water if needed. Add the cream and biltong and simmer for 5–10 minutes.

Purée using a stick blender and serve immediately.

Yields 4 servings at 7.5 g carbs per serving.

Biltong, bacon and baby marrow soup

Coconut oil for frying
1 x 250 g packet streaky bacon
1 handful fairly wet, fatty biltong
(or spiced steak strips)
8–10 baby marrows, grated
1 x 400 ml can coconut cream
½ cup fresh cream
2 cups water or Bone Broth (p. 65)
1 tsp crushed garlic
Salt and black pepper to taste
½ bunch chopped fresh chives
(optional)

Heat a little coconut oil in a medium-size saucepan. Chop the bacon into bite-size pieces and fry with the biltong or steak for 1–2 minutes.

Add the baby marrows and sauté with the meat pieces for 2–3 minutes. Add the rest of the ingredients and simmer for 7–8 minutes or until the baby marrows break down a bit into the soup.

Adjust the thickness of the soup by adding more water if needed.

Yields 4 servings at 8 g carbs per serving.

Biltong, bacon and baby marrow soup

Food for Kids

Baby food

NOT VERY MANY PEOPLE REALISE THAT A BABY WHO NURSES ON BREAST MILK IS IN FACT ALREADY IN
A KETO-ADAPTED STATE – BASICALLY, USING FAT AS THE PRIMARY FUELLING SYSTEM. BREAST MILK CONSISTS
OF FOUR VERY IMPORTANT DIETARY COMPONENTS:

Proteins

Human milk contains about 60 per cent whey and 40 per cent casein. The whey protein helps to protect against infection. Human milk proteins also contribute a lot to the first programming of a healthy gut bacteria system.

Fats

Human milk contains excellent sources of fats crucial for primary energy as well as brain and nervous system development and growth. During the last trimester, long-chain fatty acids are actually being deposited in the infant's brain and these are supplemented further with breast milk after birth.

Vitamins

A well-nourished mom will have a rich variety of vitamins to offer her baby via breast milk. Making carb-smart choices and eating nutrient-dense foods, rather than empty, sugar-filled ones, is a great gift for your baby.

Carbohydrates

Lactose is the primary carbohydrate found in breast milk and is a secondary source of energy. Lactose also contributes to healthy gut development, which forms the body's disease-fighting defence force.

Breast-feeding is advised for at least the first six months to a year. During this time, the infant's fragile new system can be well established.

Why am I giving you Breast Milk 101, you may wonder? When it comes to first foods, and later introducing solids, I think it makes sense to stay within the primary preferred fuelling system boundaries when it comes to food transitions. You can also see that sugar plays an almost miniscule role in breast milk nutrition. We need to take this as a big hint! Believe me, the idea is harder for you to grasp than for your baby. You can only miss something you already know...

However, always check with your medical caregiver first. I am not a licenced medical professional. Whatever I write here is based on my personal experience, research, and possibly the experience of others. I am not making any medical claims. So take what I write and consult with your trusted practitioner before making any changes.

This chapter will give you wheat-free, sugar-free baby food options that will be easy to slot in with the pantry ingredients of the rest of the family.

First foods (4–6 months)

WHY NOT GO THE BABY CEREAL ROUTE FOR FIRST FOODS? BABIES DO NOT HAVE SUFFICIENT AMOUNTS OF THE PROPER ENZYME, CALLED AMYLASE, NEEDED TO BREAK DOWN GRAINS IN THEIR TUMMIES. IMPROPERLY DIGESTED RICE AND OTHER STARCHY FOODS WILL CREATE INFLAMMATION THAT CAN PAVE THE WAY TO FOOD ALLERGIES IN CHILDHOOD AND TRIGGER THE FORMATION OF AUTO-ANTIBODIES ASSOCIATED WITH DIABETES LATER IN LIFE. INTRODUCE ONE FOOD AT A TIME FOR A FEW DAYS TO SEE IF THERE ARE ANY FOOD ALLERGY REACTIONS. TALK TO YOUR HEALTH-CARE PROVIDER AS SOON AS YOU SUSPECT A CERTAIN FOOD TO BE A TRIGGER.

First food suggestions

Avocado is a great source of protein, fats, vitamins and carbohydrates. It is a convenient, complete first baby food. Simply pop an avo into your baby bag along with a zip-seal bag, small bowl and spoon. Mash a tiny bit until very smooth and then pop the rest back into the refrigerator for a salad later.

Other good first food choices would be: Puréed gem squash, carrot, spinach, pumpkin, baby marrow and butternut.

Steam or cook the veggies in a saucepan on medium heat, and then purée using a stick blender. Incorporate some cooled boiled water to prevent the purée from being lumpy and to achieve a more fluid consistency.

Spoon into a few zip-seal bags with the food and date specified. Keep in the refrigerator for no more than 2–3 days. These are handy for a grab-and-go meal in a flash. Serve at room temperature or heat slightly on the stovetop.

Second foods (7–9 months)

YOU CAN GRADUALLY START TO INCORPORATE MASHED COMBINATIONS, BLENDED WITH A BONE BROTH BASE. NOW IS ALSO A GOOD TIME TO INCORPORATE SOME FRUIT BUT BE AWARE THAT IF YOU GET YOUR BABY USED TO MASHED FRUIT BEFORE BROCCOLI, BROCCOLI MAY NEVER FULLY INTEGRATE INTO THE MENU. ALWAYS INTRODUCE A NEW FOOD, FOR EXAMPLE BROCCOLI, IN COMBINATION WITH A FIRST FOOD YOU HAVE TRIED SUCCESSFULLY BEFORE.

Second food combination suggestions

Bone broth is something you may not readily associate with baby food, but it adds a giant nutritional component that simply makes a lot of sense. Bone broth serves as a digestive elixir. It helps the lining of a baby's digestive tract to mature and strengthen so that your baby can get ready to digest more complex foods. It is a sensible early choice to add to baby food.

DIY bone broth for baby

Make your own bone broth using 3–4 free-range chicken wings, 1 small carrot, ½ onion, 1 celery stick and 1 Tbsp apple cider vinegar. Add 8 cups water and cook on low heat for 2–3 hours or more. Strain and allow to cool. Freeze in ice-cube trays and then store in a zip-seal bag until you are ready to pop a cube of broth into a warm, just-cooked batch of baby food.

Try these combinations

- Hard-boiled free-range egg yolk with 1–2 tsp bone broth to make a softer consistency. (The white of the egg contains some food allergens. Only introduce in later months.)
- Mashed broccoli and baby marrow with a few tablespoons bone broth.
- Mashed hard-boiled free-range egg yolk, butternut and cauliflower with a few tablespoons bone broth.
- Mashed pumpkin with steamed blueberries.
- Mashed baby marrow with a small piece of puréed chicken.

- Baby marrow and steamed blueberry mash.
- Mashed green beans and pumpkin with puréed beef mince.
- Mashed fresh papaya and carrot.
- Mashed spinach, cauliflower and bone broth with puréed lamb.
- Mashed gem squash and apple purée.

Preparation guide

Steam, bake or cook most fruit and all veggies in a saucepan or food steamer on medium heat, and purée with a stick blender, food processor or fork. Always use a larger ratio of veggies to fruit to balance the carbs and keep food from being too watery.

When adding meat to prepared vegetables, simply cook or boil the meat in water without any spices. Meat should be 100 per cent cooked. Chop the cooked meat into small cubes and add a little of the cooking water/broth. Purée with a stick blender, blender or food processor before adding the meat sauce to the prepared veggies. Check to make sure that there are no large lumps left.

Label, date and bag. Most of these combos, except the avocado and fruit combos, will keep well in the refrigerator for 2–3 days, or freeze them for longer and simply thaw at room temperature.

Introduce baby to flax cereal

Introduce a bit of Creamy Porridge (p. 40) during this stage. Serve with coconut milk if you are not ready to introduce dairy yet.

Use up to 1 Tbsp of flax per day, but note that it is important to ease baby into flax consumption. You can also sprinkle a tiny bit of flax meal over your baby's veggies and fruit purées.

Always grind flaxseeds from scratch in your coffee grinder and use right away to benefit from the omega-3 goodness.

Third foods (9–12 months)

YOU WILL FIND IT MUCH EASIER TO ALLOW YOUR BABY TO EAT FINELY CUT OR MASHED TABLE FOODS WITH THE REST OF THE FAMILY. I HAVE INCLUDED A FEW KIDDIE-FRIENDLY, FAMILY RECIPES IN THIS BOOK SPECIFICALLY FOR THIS PURPOSE (SEE MAINS, PP. 95–103). FOR THE REST OF THE TIME, THERE ARE FUN FINGER FOODS TO BE INTRODUCED! EATING TABLE FOOD WILL ALSO ALLOW A BIT OF DAIRY, SOME BUTTER OR COCONUT OIL AND CREAM INTO YOUR BABY'S DIET.

Finger food suggestions

Fats

Avocado pieces, egg yolk quarters, grated cheese, cheese sticks, cream cheese to spread on low-carb bread cubes or to scoop on a veggie cube.

Proteins

Cooked and diced chicken pieces and soft, stewed meat pieces the size of peas, small cubes of buttered low-carb bread or muffins.

Carbs

Steamed or baked veggie cubes or pieces, blueberries, chopped steamed strawberries, soft melon and watermelon cubes, baked or steamed apple cubes.

Fourth foods (12+ months) a.k.a. spoon foods or allergy-prone foods

At this point your baby will be ready to take matters and spoons into his or her own hands! Continue to introduce more allergy-prone foods such as scrambled eggs, nut-based breads and muffin pieces, one at a time.

Make your own flavoured yoghurts using plain double-cream yoghurt and a tablespoon of fruit purée. And introduce some soft, chewy cookies from this book (pp. 185–186).

Feel good that your baby is grain free, sugar free and 'happee'!

Lunchbox love

PACKING LCHF LUNCHBOXES DOES NOT HAVE TO BE STRESSFUL AT ALL, ALTHOUGH MANY PEOPLE MAY DOUBT THAT THEY WILL BE ABLE TO GET THEIR KIDS FULL WITHOUT USING COMMERCIAL BREAD AS THE BASE OF THE LUNCHBOX. PACKING 'SMART FUEL' IN THE FORM OF NUTRIENT-DENSE FOODS IS THE ANSWER.
THESE ARE EXAMPLES OF COMBINATIONS I FEED MY TWO GROWING PRE-TEENS DAILY. THEY ALWAYS ASSURE ME THAT I AM CLOSER TO OVERFEEDING THEM THAN STARVING THEM, SO IT'S GOING TO BE FINE! USE THESE IDEAS FOR YOUR LUNCHBOXES AND MIX AND MATCH ACCORDING TO YOUR SCHEDULE AND FOOD PREFERENCES. THAT OLD SANDWICH FROM THE PAST GAVE WAY LESS ENERGY THAN WHAT YOU ARE ABOUT TO PACK IN:

THE DRUMMER BOY
2 cooked free-range chicken drumsticks
3 cucumber and cream cheese 'sandwiches' (6 slices cucumber sandwiched with cream cheese)
1 boiled egg
3 No-Bake chocolate rum balls (p. 190)
(use rum essence, not rum)

THE LOONY BOX
4 Mini Meatballs (p. 56), cocktail tomatoes and cheese cubes on 2 sticks
Veggie sticks and avocado dip
2–3 Blackberry Poppers (p. 182)

THE NUTTY BUDDY
Nut Butter (p. 24), celery sticks and 3–4 apple slices
Basic Bread Sandwich (p. 148) with meat and cheese filling

THE BERRY NICE ONE
1 Tbsp Berry Jam (p. 136) in double-cream yoghurt in a small jar
Chicken and Cheese Cupcake (p. 55)
Savoury Muffin (p. 43)
3–4 baby carrots

THE OLA AMIGO
Beef wrap (Breakfast Wrap, p. 45) with grated Cheddar and mince
Cocktail tomatoes and sugar snap peas
2 Brain Booster Bar squares (p. 189)

THE BOERIE BOX
Boerie roll (p. 103) with Tomato Sauce (p. 136)
Cheese cubes
Cucumber sticks and 3 fresh strawberries

THE YANKEE BOX
2 cheese burgers on a stick (mini beef patties, 4 cheese squares, 2 bacon rashers cut to the same size as the cheese, 2 cocktail tomatoes and 2 sosatie sticks)
Veggie sticks
Chocolate Brownie (p. 179)

THE PIP PIP CHEERIO
Mini Quiche (p. 55)
Cucumber and salami sandwiches (3 slices mini salami, 6 slices cucumber sandwiched with cream cheese)
2 Brain Booster Bar squares (p. 189)

THE LAZY MOMMA
3 rashers bacon
1 boiled egg
Veggie sticks
Amasi-and-berry smoothie

THE BUSHVELD BUFFALO
Biltong pieces and droëwors pieces
Cheese sandwich made with low-carb bread
Veggie sticks
Apple slices, with Quick Caramel Syrup (p. 180) in a separate container

THE IT'S AMORE!

2 slices Breakfast Pizza (p. 44)

Veggie sticks

Jelly (use Simply Delish natural jelly) and whipped cream in a bowl

THE LE BISTRO

Roast beef, mustard and cream cheese open sandwich made with Four-Seeds Bread (p. 152)

Cocktail tomatoes and cucumber sticks

No-Bake Caramel Cream Cheese Balls (p. 190)

THE FINGER FOOD BOX

Boerewors wheels and cheese blocks, with Pink Sauce (p. 139) in a separate container

Nut Butter (p. 24) and celery sticks

Fruit kebab

THE PIG IN A BLANKET

Quality sausage (not processed meat), cut open, stuffed with cheese and wrapped with bacon and cooked

Basic Bread Hot Dog Bun (p. 148), with condiments of your choice

Veggie sticks

Plain double-cream yoghurt with Berry Jam (p. 136)

THE SNOOKER BALL BOX

Meatballs with breadsticks and Pink Sauce (p. 139) in a separate container

Veggie sticks

Small handful nuts

LEKKER TIPS

- I always make a batch or two of certain foods or baked goods in advance and spread it over a few days.
- When you make a mince dish for dinner, make a few extra mini hamburger patties or meatballs to pop into lunchboxes the following day.
- Make a few kilograms of meatballs, boerewors, chicken drumsticks and chicken and cheese cupcakes and freeze in quantities that will suit your family. Thaw at room temperature and assemble.
- Mini quiche, muffins, brownies, basic buns and breads stay fresh in the refrigerator for 3–4 days and can also be frozen. Thaw at room temperature.
- One Saturday afternoon and a little forward planning can take care of most of your lunchbox needs for the week ahead.

Kids' party food

Pirate's Treasure

Where's me eye patch? cupcakes

Prepare the Sponge Cake Cupcakes and Icing (p. 173). Secure an eye patch (purchased from a novelty, party or toy store) upright in each cupcake.

Hidden treasure cups – jelly parfait

Use 2 or 3 Simply Delish natural jelly flavours.

Pack out some see-through plastic cups.

Cut a strawberry or red pepper into strips and pack a red X at the bottom of each cup. Add one flavour layer of jelly at a time, allowing each layer to set before adding the next.

Top with whipped cream and decorate with sprinkles or chocolate shavings.

Pirate platter

Canon balls – Use Mini Meatballs of your choice (p. 56)
Peg legs – Cooked chicken drumsticks
Veggie sticks and dip
Cheese cubes

Pink Polka Dot Tea Party

Strawberry jewels

Cut 10 strawberries in half. Slice off the roundest part of the skin in order to allow the strawberry to sit flat and not roll like a boat at sea.

Make a half-quantity of the Lemon Cheesecake Mousse (p. 163). Spoon it into a piping bag and swirl like soft serve onto the strawberry base. Chill and arrange on your table in a pretty manner and add a polka dot label to describe each element on the birthday table.

Dotty brownies (see Chocolate Brownie recipe, p. 179)

After the brownies have cooled, take a round cookie cutter and cut out as many 'dotty brownies' as possible.

Make a Berry Mousse (p. 163) and spoon it into a piping bag. Cover the brownies with a decadent swirl of mousse. Decorate with finely grated 85% dark chocolate shavings.

The queen's pearls

Choose a Mini Meatball recipe (p. 56). Thread a meatball and a cherry tomato onto a toothpick and arrange on a pretty serving dish. The meatball needs to be below the tomato so you can easily dip it into the Pink Sauce Dip (p. 139).

Veggie and cheese flowers

The flower: Use 1 large carrot, peeled and cut into 0.5 cm thick coins. Use a small flower-shaped cookie cutter to cut the coins into flowers. If you don't have a cookie cutter, you can cut out two small triangles from the coins to form a mini tulip. Use a few cocktail tomatoes on their own for pretty little red flowers.

The leaves: Halve and deseed a third of an English cucumber. Cut into 1 cm thick slices to form the leaves. Now stick a toothpick through the centre of the cucumber skin side and thread the little carrot and tomato flowers on top. The leaves will point upwards.

Take a few cubes of cheese and use as a stand for the flower.

No-bake caramel cream cheese balls with glitter dusting

Prepare the No-bake Caramel Cream Cheese Balls (p. 190). Place some edible bright glitter sprinkles in a bowl, and dip the cheese balls into the glitter instead of the coconut.

Mains

Stuffed angelfish

4 Tbsp coconut oil

4–6 yellow patty pans, sliced

2 fresh angelfish (ask your fish-monger to debone and butterfly them. You want the top fin side attached so you can stuff it with all kinds of awesomeness)

2 Tbsp butter

1 cup grated Cheddar cheese

1 tomato, thinly sliced

1 medium onion, sliced

1 Tbsp crushed garlic

Salt and pepper to taste

Squeeze of lemon

Preheat the oven to 180 °C.

Heat a little of the coconut oil in a pan on medium–low heat and fry the patty pans slowly until browned on both sides. Set aside.

Place a large sheet of foil in an ovenproof dish and drizzle with a little more coconut oil.

Place the fish on the foil and stuff it with the butter, cheese, to-mato, onion and garlic. Add seasoning. Cover with the overlapping foil and bake for 20 minutes. Open the foil and test if the fish is ready by inserting a knife. The knife should slip right into the thickest part of the fish and the tip should feel warm to the touch. Also check to see if the filling has melted properly.

Drizzle the rest of the coconut oil over the fish and grill for 2–3 minutes until lightly browned.

Layer the patty pans on top of the fish and add a quick squeeze of lemon. Serve immediately.

Yields 4–6 servings (4 servings = 5.3 g carbs per serving, 6 servings = 3.5 g carbs per serving).

Moroccan lamb and lemon tagine

A TAGINE IS A MOROCCAN STEW MADE IN A TAGINE POT. LUCKILY YOU CAN ALSO MAKE THIS DISH IN THE OVEN IN A CASSEROLE DISH AFTER YOU HAVE BROWNED THE MEAT. AND IF YOU CAN FIND SOME SAFFRON, A FEW STRANDS WILL TAKE THIS STEW TO A NEW LEVEL.

2 Tbsp coconut oil or lard
1 kg stewing lamb
1 tsp salt
2 Tbsp crushed garlic
1 onion, chopped
2 Tbsp Moroccan Spice (p. 135)
4–6 cups water
Juice of ½ lemon
1 cinnamon stick
¼ cabbage, shredded
1 tomato, chopped
2 cups cubed pumpkin
1 Tbsp xylitol
4 Tbsp butter
Grated zest of 1 lemon

Heat the coconut oil in a heavy-bottomed saucepan on medium high heat and brown the lamb for a few minutes. Add a sprinkle of salt and the garlic.

After a few minutes of browning, add the onion and Moroccan Spice mix and sauté until the onion is soft. Add half of the water, the lemon juice, and the cinnamon stick. Simmer for 1–1½ hours on very low heat, topping up the water if needed.

Once the meat is tender and easy to separate from the bones, add the cabbage, tomato and pumpkin, xylitol, butter and the lemon zest. Top up with water and adjust the spices to taste. Cook with the lid mostly on until the veggies are soft and the liquids have reduced enough to moisten the stew without being watery.

Serve over any mash of your choice.

Yields 6 hearty servings at 8 g carbs per serving.

Thai chicken curry

2 Tbsp coconut oil
4 free-range chicken breasts, skin on,
deboned and cut into strips or chunks
Herbal salt or salt and black pepper
½ yellow pepper, cut into strips
½ red pepper, cut into strips
1 cup sliced mushrooms of choice
1 handful mange tout
5 baby marrows, sliced
1 x 400 ml can coconut cream
5–6 dried lime leaves
1 tsp crushed garlic
1 Tbsp green curry paste, red curry paste
or panang curry paste
Chopped fresh coriander or spring onion
to garnish

Heat the coconut oil in a pan and stir-fry the chicken strips for 2–3 minutes on medium–high heat until browned. Add salt and pepper to taste.

Add all the veggies and sauté for 2–3 minutes. Add the coconut cream, lime leaves, garlic and curry paste. Simmer for 10–15 minutes on low heat.

Discard the lime leaves and serve in deep bowls, garnished with coriander or spring onion.

Yields 4 servings at 9 g carbs per serving.

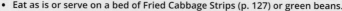

 LEKKER TIPS

- Eat as is or serve on a bed of Fried Cabbage Strips (p. 127) or green beans.
- I sometimes add 1 cup of water with the coconut cream and then serve this dish as a soup.
- You can exchange the chicken for any kind of cubed meat, and feel free to vary the veggies and curry paste to your heart's content.
- This makes an awesome prawn curry too!

Moroccan chicken and almond pastilla

A PASTILLA IS A MOROCCAN PIE WITH A DISTINCT SWEET CINNAMON AND NUTTY FLAVOUR PROFILE. IT IS A TRULY MEMORABLE DISH THAT I FELL IN LOVE WITH A FEW YEARS AGO. IT WAS QUITE A CHALLENGE TO 'DECARB' PHYLLO PASTRY, BUT WHERE THERE IS A WILL, THERE IS A WAY!

FILLING
8 cooked free-range chicken pieces, deboned and chopped
2 spring onions, chopped
1 tsp ground cinnamon
1 tsp ground ginger
1 tsp turmeric
Salt to taste
1 Tbsp grated orange zest
2 Tbsp orange juice
2 Tbsp butter

NUT LAYER
1 Tbsp coconut oil
1 x 100 g packet flaked almonds
1 Tbsp xylitol
1 tsp ground cinnamon

PIE SHELL
6 free-range eggs
Pinch salt
½ x 230 g block cream cheese
½ cup desiccated coconut (milled in a coffee grinder)
1 tsp xylitol
Coconut oil for frying

TOPPING
3 Tbsp butter, melted
3 Tbsp xylitol, powdered in your coffee grinder
Sprinkle of cinnamon

For the filling, place all the ingredients in a heavy-bottomed saucepan on high heat and sauté for 3–4 minutes to allow all the flavours to infuse. Set aside.

Next prepare the nut layer. Melt the coconut oil in a pan on medium heat and fry the almond flakes, xylitol and cinnamon for a minute or two. The nuts must be browned slightly but not burnt. Set aside.

For the pie shell, mix the eggs, salt and cream cheese together in a food processor until all the cream cheese clumps are dissolved. Give the desiccated coconut a quick whizz in the grinder and add to the egg mix along with the xylitol.

Melt some coconut oil in a pan on high heat and pour in enough batter to cover the base of the pan. You want the batter to be only a few millimetres thick (basically, the thickness of a pancake or tortilla). As soon as the batter has settled and you can easily insert a spatula under the wrap, lift up a corner to see if it has browned enough and then flip. Remove from the pan and keep warm while you make the rest. You need 4–6 wraps.

Now get a 10 cm ramekin and gently line it with 1 wrap. The wrap will be quite a bit bigger than the ramekin, so allow the extra to overlap the sides. Add a layer of filling and top with a layer of nuts. Repeat a layer of filling and a layer of nuts. Compact the four layers with your palm, being careful not to tear the wrap. Now fold the overlapping edges of the wrap over the last layer in a neat pleat-like manner. There will be a slight hole in the centre of your fold-over pie. Place a knob of butter over the hole. The butter will help to keep the pie sealed. Now gently tip the pie into your hand and place butter side down onto a baking tray. Repeat with the rest of the pastillas.

Preheat the oven to 180 °C. Brush the pies with melted butter and bake for 10–12 minutes. You want the pie to be slightly browned and crunchy. As soon as the pies come out of the oven, give a dusting with the powdered xylitol and a sprinkle of cinnamon. Serve with any veggie side or Salted Pumpkin Fries (p. 101).

Yields 4–6 servings (4 servings = 13 g carbs per serving, 6 servings = 9 g carbs per serving).

Pork chops in a mustard cream sauce

4–6 pork chops (preferably thick)
Salt and pepper to taste
1 tsp dried thyme
2 Tbsp coconut oil or lard for frying
1 quantity Mustard Cream Sauce
(p. 143)

Season the chops with salt and pepper and rub in some dried thyme.

In a griddle pan or skillet on medium to high heat, melt the oil or lard and arrange the pork chops in the pan (do this in batches if your pan isn't big enough). Turn the chops every 2 minutes or so, making sure all the sides are nicely grilled – 10–15 minutes should be enough for thicker cut pork chops. Serve with the mustard cream sauce.

Yields 4–6 servings (4 servings = 2.5 g carbs per serving, 6 servings = 1.7 g carbs per serving).

Pumpkin gnocchi with bacon and sage cream

GNOCCHI
1 free-range egg
½ x 230 g block cream cheese, at room temperature
1 cup cooked, mashed pumpkin, still warm
4 Tbsp psyllium husks
½ cup almond meal
Pinch salt and pepper

BACON AND SAGE CREAM
2 Tbsp coconut oil
3 spring onions, chopped
1 x 250 g punnet mushrooms, sliced
1 tsp crushed garlic
Salt and pepper to taste
1 x 250 g packet diced bacon, fried until crisp (or cooked chicken)
12 rosa tomatoes, halved
4–5 fresh sage leaves, chopped or 1 tsp dried sage
1 cup fresh cream
1 cup grated Cheddar cheese

For the gnocchi, beat the egg and cream cheese together until fluffy. Add the rest of the ingredients and mix well, using a fork, for about a minute or so. Allow the batter to thicken and cool for 10 minutes.

Form the batter into a sausage shape on a buttered surface or glass cutting board. Cut into four equal strips. Now roll each strip into a thicker snake shape and then cut into 8–10 pieces.

Fry 8–10 gnocchi at a time in a pan barely covered in coconut oil and make sure to turn regularly in order to brown all sides. Repeat with the rest of the gnocchi and then allow to cool and set.

For the cream topping, heat the coconut oil in a heavy-bottomed saucepan on medium–high and sauté the spring onions, mushrooms and garlic for 3–4 minutes until the mushrooms are tender. Add salt and pepper to taste. Add the bacon or chicken pieces, tomatoes, sage and cream. Allow ingredients to infuse and simmer gently on low heat for 3–5 minutes. Stir in the grated cheese and allow a minute or two for the cheese to melt and thicken the sauce somewhat.

Scoop onto the gnocchi portions while still hot in order to reheat the gnocchi.

Yields 4 servings at 12 g carbs per serving.

LEKKER TIPS

- Make your favourite pasta sauce and scoop it over the gnocchi to reheat it.
- These make great toddler snacks too. Just grate some cheese over and there you go!

Pumpkin gnocchi with bacon and sage cream

Cauli mac and cheese

All the recipes that follow are quick, kid-friendly mains.

Chicken à la less carbs

2 Tbsp coconut oil
8–10 free-range chicken pieces
2 Tbsp lemon juice
Salt and black pepper to taste
2–3 cups water
1 x 250 g punnet mushrooms, sliced
8 baby marrows, sliced
3 spring onions, sliced
1 tsp crushed garlic
1 Tbsp butter
1 cup fresh cream

Heat the coconut oil in a heavy-bottomed saucepan on medium heat and brown the chicken pieces. Add the lemon juice, seasoning and water and cook on medium heat until the chicken can easily be removed from the bones. Top up water if necessary.

Remove from heat and drain most of the liquid into a separate container. Debone the chicken and return the meat to the saucepan along with the sliced veggies, garlic and more seasoning. Add the butter and sauté the chicken and veggies, allowing the veggies to caramelise ever so slightly. Add the cream and 1 cup of the drained liquid. Simmer on medium heat until the veggies are soft and the sauce has reduced a bit. Add more salt and pepper to taste. Serve on any mash combination of your choice (p. 127) or eat as a 'stoup' (stew–soup).

Yields 4–5 servings (4 servings = 6 g carbs per serving, 5 servings = 4.6 g carbs per serving).

Cauli mac and cheese

1 large head cauliflower
4 Tbsp butter
Salt and pepper to taste
2 tsp crushed garlic
1 cup fresh cream (or double cream if available)
1 x 250 g packet streaky bacon
500 g quality beef mince (not lean)
½ cup water
1 x 115 g can tomato purée
1 Tbsp apple cider vinegar
2 tsp xylitol
1 tsp dried mixed herbs
1 free-range egg
¾ cup grated Cheddar cheese

Preheat the oven to 180 °C.

Cut the cauliflower into florets and then cut each floret lengthwise into a few strips. You want it to have the basic length of a macaroni noodle. Heat the butter in a heavy-bottomed saucepan on medium heat and sauté the cauli strips with some salt, pepper and 1 tsp garlic. Allow to caramelise a bit, but don't allow it to go mushy. Transfer into an ovenproof dish and pour all the pan juices over the cauliflower. Pour ½ cup cream over the cauli layer. Set aside.

Fry the bacon rashers in the same saucepan in which you cooked the cauliflower. Roughly chop the bacon and set aside in a separate bowl. Brown the mince in the same saucepan and then add the water, tomato purée, remaining 1 tsp garlic, the vinegar, xylitol, herbs and salt and pepper to taste. Simmer and reduce until it forms a thick meat sauce, otherwise it will make your dish watery.

Layer the meat sauce over the cauli layer and top with bacon pieces. In a jug, mix the remaining ½ cup cream, the egg and ½ cup grated cheese together. Pour over the meat layer. Sprinkle the rest of the cheese over the top and bake until 'oozy', browned and cheesy soft. Serve with a salad and a small, low-carb Garlic Loaf (p. 148).

Yields 4 servings at 8 g carbs per serving.

Stuffed meatballs in marinara sauce

600–700 g beef mince
12–15 mozzarella cubes (about the size of a jawbreaker)
3 Tbsp coconut oil
Salt and pepper
1 x 410 g can whole tomatoes in juice
1 Tbsp crushed garlic
1 tsp dried mixed herbs
1 Tbsp xylitol
1 Tbsp apple cider vinegar
7 Tbsp fresh cream
1 cup grated Cheddar cheese

Shape the mince into meatballs slightly bigger than a golf ball. Stuff each meatball with a cube of mozzarella and roll the meatball firmly to make sure it is sealed properly after inserting the cheese.

Heat the coconut oil in a heavy-bottomed saucepan on medium heat and fry the meatballs. Season the meatballs in the saucepan while turning often. As soon as the meatballs are browned on most sides, add the canned tomatoes, garlic, mixed herbs, xylitol and vinegar.

Turn the heat to low and simmer for 10–15 minutes while the meatballs cook in the lovely sauce. Add a bit of water if the sauce seems to be reducing too quickly.

Add the cream and simmer on low heat with the lid on for another 5–8 minutes.

Scoop the meatballs and sauce over sautéed ribbons of baby marrows, shredded cabbage, Cauli–Green Bean Mash (p. 109) or creamed spinach, and top with grated cheese.

Yields 4–6 servings (4 servings = 7.3 g carbs per serving, 6 servings = 5 g carbs per serving).

Chicken pie

CRUST
¾ cup almond flour
1 tsp baking powder
6 Tbsp cold butter
1 cup cream cheese, at room temperature
2 free-range eggs

FILLING
1 quantity Chicken à la Less Carbs (p. 95), but swap the baby marrows for ½ chopped onion, and add a sprinkle of nutmeg, ¼ tsp ground cloves, 1 tsp dried or a handful fresh thyme sprigs, 1 Tbsp chopped fresh parsley and 4 whole peppercorns or a few grinds of your favourite herb blend

Preheat the oven to 180 °C.

For the crust, mix the almond flour and baking powder together. Rub in the cold butter until the mixture has a lumpy crumb texture.

Blend the cream cheese with a hand mixer or food processor and add the eggs, one by one. Add the almond and butter crumbs to the liquid batter and mix gently for about 30 seconds until it makes a smooth paste.

For the filling, follow the recipe instructions but cook a bit longer on medium to high heat in order to reduce the sauce and to form a creamy, thick, chicken filling.

Spoon the filling into your pie dish. Pour the batter over the filling and bake for 15–20 minutes until puffed up and browned.

Yields 4–6 servings (4 servings = 10 g carbs per serving, 6 servings = 8.5 g carbs per serving).

Chicken pie

Fish fingers

Fish fingers

FISH FINGERS

750 g fresh hake (ask your fish-monger to clean and fillet them)

4 free-range eggs

1½ cups desiccated coconut (fine or medium shreds)

Salt and pepper to taste

Coconut oil for frying

CHUNKY TARTAR SAUCE

1 cup Creamy Mayo (p. 139)

½ yellow pepper, finely chopped

1 small red onion, finely chopped

2 spring onions, finely chopped

1 small tomato, finely chopped

1 tsp Tomato Sauce (p. 136) (optional)

For the fish fingers, cut the hake fillets into 3-cm-thick steaks.

Beat the eggs together in a bowl. Place the coconut in a flat dish or on a large plate and season it with salt and pepper.

Add enough coconut oil to cover the base of a frying pan to about 5 mm deep and set on medium–high heat.

Dip the fish pieces into the beaten egg first and then roll in coconut. Repeat once more. Fry for 6–8 minutes in total, turning as soon as the coconut crust has settled and browned on one side. Turn every 2 minutes or so. If you are not sure just break one of the strips in half. The fish should have a flaky texture.

For the tartar sauce, mix all the ingredients together. Serve the sauce with the fish fingers and a salad or coleslaw. I sometimes add Salted Pumpkin Fries (p. 101) on the side.

Yields 4 servings at 8 g carbs per serving.

Chicken nuggets or strips

USE THE RECIPE ABOVE, SIMPLY REPLACING THE FISH WITH CHICKEN FILLETS CUT INTO NUGGET CHUNKS OR LONG, 2-CM-THICK STRIPS.

 LEKKER TIPS

- Grind the coconut, some grated Parmesan cheese and 1 tsp dried mixed herbs in your coffee grinder for a more breadcrumb-like coating.

Squash surprise cups

KIDS LOVE FOOD WITH A STORY ATTACHED SO WHY NOT CREATE SOME TO SNEAK IN MORE VEGGIES? THESE LITTLE SURPRISE CUPS WILL TURN EATING VEGGIES INTO AN ADVENTURE. YOU CAN PREPARE AS MANY AS YOU NEED, SO SPECIFIC QUANTITIES ARE NOT GIVEN HERE.

Halved and cooked gem squash, seeds removed
1 knob butter for each squash half

FAIRIES IN THE FOREST SURPRISE
Salami strips or mince in tomato sauce (the soil)
Steamed broccoli florets (the trees)
A few toasted sunflower seeds (fairy shoes)
Grated cheese (the sun shining on the trees)

LOST DINOSAUR EGGS SURPRISE
Cooked chicken fillet, cut into smaller cubes (the dino eggs)
Creamed spinach (the swamp)
Grated cheese (the sun shining on the swampy water)

Fill the squash and place under a preheated oven grill until the cheese has melted.

Count about 3 g carbs per half surprise cup.

Pirate pepperoni pizza ships

Medium baby marrows, halved lengthways and seeds scooped out
2 Tbsp melted coconut oil
Salt and pepper to taste
1 x 410 g can chopped tomatoes (you will use only a few tablespoons)
Grated mozzarella cheese
1 cabanossi or salami stick, thinly sliced

Preheat the oven to 180 °C.

Place the halved baby marrows on a wax paper-lined baking tray. Brush the melted coconut oil over the marrows and sprinkle with salt and pepper. Bake for 10–12 minutes until the marrows are soft. Remove tray from oven and preheat the oven grill.

Top the marrows with chopped tomato, mozzarella and the 'pepperoni' slices. Place under the grill until the cheese melts and bubbles.

Make a sail from a scrap piece of paper and a toothpick and insert into the marrows to complete the pirate ship.

Count about 3.5 g carbs per pizza boat.

Baby marrow fries with Parmesan

6–8 baby marrows, quartered lengthways
4 Tbsp melted coconut oil
Garlic and herb grinder mix or salt and pepper to taste
½ cup grated Parmesan cheese

Preheat the oven to 180 °C. Brush the marrows with the coconut oil. Sprinkle with seasoning and Parmesan. Spread out the coated marrows in a single layer on a wax paper-lined baking tray. Bake for 15 minutes or until cooked through. Turn on the grill and grill the fries for 5 minutes until the cheese is brown and crispy. Turn the fries a few times to grill evenly.

Yields 4 servings at about 2 g carbs per serving.

Salted pumpkin fries

400 g fresh pumpkin sticks (you get ready-made ones in the fresh produce aisle)
4 Tbsp melted coconut oil
Moroccan Spice (p. 135) or any spices of choice

Preheat the oven to 180 °C. Brush the pumpkin sticks well with the melted oil. Sprinkle with your chosen spice mix and place in a single layer on a wax paper-lined baking tray. Bake for 20 minutes or until the pumpkin is cooked through. Turn on the grill and brown the fries for 5–10 minutes or until the edges are crispy. Turn the fries a few times for all-round crispiness.

Yields 4 servings at 5 g carbs per serving.

Pork burger

Burgers

BURGERS ARE BACK ON THE LOW-CARB MENU USING ANY OF THESE OPTIONS FOR THE BURGER BUN: GRILLED LARGE BROWN MUSHROOMS; GRILLED 2-CM-THICK BRINJAL DISCS FOR ROUND PATTIES, OR STRIPS TO FIT A CHICKEN FILLET; BREAKFAST BUNS (P. 44); BAKE YOUR OWN CRUSTY BUNS AND ROLLS USING THE BASIC BREAD RECIPE (P. 147).

To make your chosen burger patties, mix all the ingredients together and form into balls the size of a medium peach. Flatten between your palms to form a sturdy patty. Fry in lard or coconut oil or grill on the braai.

BEEF BURGER
1 kg beef mince
Your preferred barbecue spice as
a dry rub

Serve with lettuce, tomato and cheese and any one of the sauces on pp. 142–143.

Yields 8 patties at about 3 g carbs each when served with tomato, lettuce and cheese. Just add your preferred bun carb count.

LAMB BURGER
1 kg lamb mince
Rosemary leaves from 2 sprigs,
finely chopped
2 tsp crushed garlic
Salt, black pepper and lemon juice

Take the lamb to Morocco: Sprinkle with Moroccan Spice (p. 135), grill and serve with crumbled feta and fried onions.
   Take the lamb to Greece: Serve with avo and Easy Tzatziki (p. 139).

Yields 8 patties at 3–4 g carbs each. Just add your preferred bun carb count.

PORK BURGER
1 x 250 g packet bacon bits
300 g beef mince
500 g pork mince
1½ tsp fresh thyme or ½ tsp dried
½ small apple, grated (optional)
Salt and pepper to taste

Serve with fresh rocket and grilled plum tomatoes.

Yields 8 patties at 2–3 g carbs each. Just add your preferred bun carb count.

CHICKEN BURGER
4 free-range chicken fillets, sliced
in half
Salt and pepper to taste

For a plain bird, season the fillets with salt and pepper and fry in coconut oil until done. Serve with lettuce, tomato and cheese.
   Take it to Mexico: Sprinkle with Mexican Spice (p. 135) before frying. Serve with guacamole, salsa and sour cream or grated Cheddar.

Yields 8 patties at about 2 g carbs each when served with tomato, lettuce and cheese, and 4 g carbs each for the Mexican option. Just add your preferred bun carb count.

Boerie roll with *smoor*
Basic Buns (p. 148), *Smoor* (p. 114) and your favourite boerewors or sausage, cooked in a pan or on the grill.

Traditional South African Meals

Curry and 'cauli rice' with a tangy chutney

CURRY
1 Tbsp coconut oil
½ medium onion, chopped
2 tsp crushed garlic
1 tsp ground cinnamon
1 tsp ground ginger
2½ tsp mild curry powder
700 g beef mince
1 x 115 g can tomato purée
1 cup water
2 cups sliced green beans
½ x 400 g packet cubed pumpkin
2 Tbsp apple cider vinegar
Salt and pepper to taste

YELLOW 'CAULI RICE'
2 Tbsp butter
1 cauliflower, chopped in a food processor
Salt to taste
1 tsp turmeric

TANGY CHUTNEY
½ red pepper
½ apple
½ medium onion
1 tsp crushed garlic
1 tsp xylitol
3 Tbsp water
Salt and pepper to taste
1 tsp psyllium husks

For the curry, heat the coconut oil in a saucepan on medium heat and sauté the onion, garlic, cinnamon, ginger and curry powder together for 2–3 minutes. Add the beef mince and allow to brown slightly. Add the tomato purée and stir.

Add the water, green beans, pumpkin, vinegar, salt and pepper. Simmer for 15–20 minutes. Top up water if needed.

While the curry is cooking, make the cauli rice. Melt the butter in a medium saucepan and sauté the chopped cauliflower, salt and turmeric together for a minute or two. Cover the saucepan with the lid and remove from heat. Allow the cauliflower to cook in the residual heat of the saucepan. Stir carefully – only enough to fluff it up.

For the chutney, chop the red pepper, apple and onion in a food processor. Place the chopped ingredients, garlic, xylitol, water and seasoning in a small saucepan and allow to simmer and thicken for 2–4 minutes. Stir in the psyllium at the very end, and then remove from heat. Serve the curry on a bed of cauli rice, with the chutney on the side.

Yields 4 servings at 16 g carbs per serving.

Bobotie and yellow cabbage with fragrant sprinkles

1 kg beef mince

SPICY CHUTNEY

4 Tbsp coconut oil
3 small onions, chopped
1 red pepper, chopped
1 yellow pepper, chopped
1 small apple, chopped
2 Tbsp xylitol
1 Tbsp turmeric
1 Tbsp mild curry powder
2 tsp ground ginger
½ tsp paprika
½ tsp ground cumin
1 Tbsp crushed garlic
1 cup water
2 Tbsp apple cider vinegar
1 Tbsp tomato purée
Salt and pepper

EGG TOPPING

½ cup full-cream milk
½ cup fresh cream
½ cup coconut milk
2 free-range eggs

YELLOW CABBAGE

¾ head cabbage
2 Tbsp butter
½ x 400 ml can coconut milk
1 tsp turmeric
Salt and pepper to taste

FRAGRANT SPRINKLES

3 Tbsp fine or medium desiccated coconut
3 Tbsp sunflower seeds
1 tsp xylitol
½ tsp ground cinnamon

For the chutney, heat the coconut oil in a pan and sauté the onions, red and yellow peppers and apple until soft.

Stir in the rest of the chutney ingredients and simmer on low heat for 5–8 minutes until the chutney reduces to a thicker consistency.

Preheat the oven to 180 °C.

Mix in the meat and let it cook slowly into the syrupy chutney mixture for 10–12 minutes. Transfer the mince mixture into an oven-proof dish.

Mix all the topping ingredients with a fork and pour over the sweet mince mixture. Bake for 30–40 minutes.

For the cabbage, slice it into small to medium-sized strips. Melt the butter in a heavy-bottomed saucepan on medium heat and sauté the cabbage. As soon as the cabbage starts to soften and caramelise, add the coconut milk and turmeric and simmer on lower heat for a few minutes. Season to taste.

For the sprinkles, toast the coconut, sunflower seeds, xylitol and cinnamon in a dry pan. As soon as the xylitol melts, stir well to incorporate the cinnamon flavour throughout.

Serve the bobotie on a bed of yellow cabbage strips and show it some love with a good sprinkle of cinnamon-infused sprinkles.

Yields 6–8 servings (6 servings = 14 g carbs per serving, 8 servings = 10.5 g carbs per serving).

Lamb shanks on cauli–green bean mash

THIS RECIPE IS PREPARED IN TWO PARTS: ON THE STOVETOP, AND IN THE OVEN. IF YOU HAVE A LARGE STOVETOP-TO-OVEN CASSEROLE DISH WITH A LID, IT WILL BE IDEAL. IF NOT, DON'T DESPAIR – YOU CAN FINISH OFF THE DISH ON THE STOVETOP TOO OR JUST USE A CASSEROLE DISH WITH A FOIL LID FOR THE SECOND PART.

SHANKS
4–6 lamb shanks
Coconut oil for browning
Salt and pepper

STOCK
3 celery sticks and leaves, chopped
3 baby carrots
1 medium onion, roughly chopped
5 marrowbones
2 Tbsp crushed garlic
2 Tbsp rosemary and lemon herbal salt
16 cups water
2 Tbsp apple cider vinegar
1 sprig fresh rosemary
2 cups red wine (optional)
50 g butter
4 Tbsp tomato purée
2 Tbsp xylitol

CAULI–GREEN BEAN MASH
1 large cauliflower, cut into florets
3–4 cups cut green beans (frozen is fine to use in this recipe)
4 Tbsp butter
Salt and black pepper

On the stovetop, on high heat, brown the lamb shanks in coconut oil. Season lightly. Remove the shanks and place on a clean surface to rest while you start on the stock.

For the stock, use the same saucepan and sauté the veggies, marrowbones and garlic with the herbal salt until the veggies are glossy and soft. Add the water, vinegar and rosemary. Simmer for 30 minutes.

Preheat the oven to 180 °C.

Remove the marrowbones and return the shanks to the dish/casserole. Add the red wine, butter, tomato purée and xylitol.

Place the dish/casserole in the oven for 3 hours. The stock will reduce and the meat will almost fall from the bone. (If you are going the stovetop route, just let it all simmer on low heat for 3 hours.)

In both cases check the liquid levels from time to time, and be prepared to top up with a bit of water if necessary.

For the mash, place the cauliflower and green beans in a saucepan and add enough water to cover half the veggies. Bring to a boil and cook until the veggies are soft and mashable. Drain the excess water and return the saucepan to medium heat. Add the butter and seasoning and mash it all together.

To serve, spoon the mash into bowls or deep plates and make a little indent in the centre. Top with a shank and smother in gravy.

Yields 4–6 servings.
With wine in recipe: 4 servings = 16 g carbs per serving,
6 servings = 10 g carbs per serving.
Without wine in recipe: 4 servings = 13 g carbs per serving,
6 servings = 8 g carbs per serving.

Waterblommetjiebredie

I LIVE IN THE BOLAND, RIGHT IN THE HEART OF WATERBLOMMETJIE VALLEY. A WATERBLOMMETJIE (LITERALLY TRANSLATED AS 'WATER FLOWER') IS AN AQUATIC PLANT THAT GROWS IN PONDS AND IS KNOWN AS CAPE PONDWEED. IT MAKES A BEAUTIFUL, GREEN BEAN-LIKE BREDIE (STEW).

1 kg lamb neck or knuckles
Coconut oil for browning
Salt and pepper to taste
2 medium onions, chopped
2 Tbsp crushed garlic
4 cups Basic Bone Broth (p. 65)
4 Tbsp lemon juice
1 tsp grated nutmeg
1½ tsp ground coriander
2 Tbsp xylitol
2 Tbsp butter
750 g fresh waterblommetjies, soaked overnight in salted water, and stems trimmed off
1 x 400 g packet or 2½ cups cubed pumpkin
2–4 cups water
Lemon slices to garnish

In a heavy-bottomed saucepan on high heat, brown the lamb in coconut oil and give a sprinkle of salt and pepper. Remove the meat from the saucepan and set aside. Using the same saucepan, sauté the onions and garlic until soft and glossy.

Return the meat to the saucepan, along with the broth, lemon juice, nutmeg, coriander, xylitol and butter and simmer gently on low heat. Cook for a good hour or more – the meat must be soft and falling off the bone.

When the meat is tender, add the waterblommetjies and pumpkin. Add enough water to allow the veggies to cook. Too much water will make the sauce very runny – rather add a bit at a time. Cook on medium heat for 15 minutes and then do a taste test. Add salt and pepper if needed. (I sometimes sneak in a spoon of barbecue spice to lift the flavours.) Cook until the waterblommetjies and pumpkin are tender.

Serve on Cauli Rice (p. 105), cauli mash or eat as a 'stoup' (stew–soup). Garnish with a slice of lemon.

Yields 4–6 servings (4 servings = 17 g carbs per serving, 6 servings = 11.5 g carbs per serving).

LEKKER TIPS

• If you are not fortunate enough to get your hands on some authentic fresh waterblommetjies, you can always use a mix of green beans and baby marrows.

Roast chicken with Cape Malay stuffing

STUFFING

½ red pepper, roughly chopped
½ yellow pepper, roughly chopped
½ apple, roughly chopped
½ medium onion, roughly chopped
1 tsp crushed garlic
1 tsp xylitol
¼ tsp mixed spice
¼ tsp turmeric
2 Tbsp butter
Salt and pepper to taste
4 Tbsp water

CHICKEN

1 x 1.5 kg free-range chicken
2 Tbsp butter
½ medium onion, thinly sliced
1 tsp crushed garlic
½ red pepper, sliced (optional)
1 fennel bulb and stalk, thinly sliced
Salt and pepper to taste
1 x 400 ml can coconut milk
Squeeze of lemon juice
1 Tbsp xylitol
1½ cups water
1 Tbsp mild curry powder
½ tsp ground cinnamon
¼ tsp ground cumin
1 tsp turmeric
4 fresh sage leaves or 1 tsp dried sage
1 x 400 g packet or 2½ cups cubed pumpkin
1 x 350 g punnet mixed baby marrows and patty pans

For the stuffing, place all the ingredients, except the water, into a small saucepan on medium heat and sauté for 3–4 minutes. Add the water and simmer for 8–10 minutes on low heat until thickened. Stuff the chicken with the mixture and string the drumsticks together.

Preheat the oven to 180 °C.

Place the stuffed chicken in a casserole dish.

In the same saucepan you used for the stuffing, melt the butter and sauté the onion, garlic, red pepper and fennel until soft. Season with salt and pepper. Spoon the mixture around the chicken.

Add the coconut milk, lemon juice, xylitol, ½ cup water, curry powder and all the spices and sage. Make sure to sprinkle some spices onto the chicken.

Cover the dish with a lid and bake for 20 minutes.

Add the pumpkin, baby marrows and patty pans to the dish. Add a bit more water to top up the fragrant coconut sauce and bake with the lid on for another 20 minutes.

Remove the lid and allow the sauce to thicken for a few minutes before switching on the grill to give the chicken and the veggies a nice brown colour.

Serve on some Fried Cabbage Strips (p. 127) and be prepared to be admired and adored!

Yields 6 servings at 13 g carbs per serving.

Pap en wors met smoor
(Crumbly porridge, sausage and tomato–onion stew)

PAP

1 free-range egg

2 Tbsp fine desiccated coconut

¾ cup almond meal

2 Tbsp psyllium husks

Pinch salt

2 tsp baking powder

1 Tbsp apple cider vinegar

½ cup boiling water

SMOOR

1 Tbsp butter, lard or coconut oil

2 small onions, sliced

1 x 410 g can tomato and onion mix

Salt and pepper to taste

1 Tbsp xylitol

1 Tbsp apple cider vinegar

For the *wors*, use your favourite boerewors, prepared on the braai (first prize) or in a pan (second prize). (Translates as: Use your favourite sausage prepared on the barbecue grill or in a pan.)

For the *pap*, crack the egg into a microwaveable mixing bowl and whisk briefly with a fork. In a separate bowl, mix the coconut, almond meal, psyllium, salt and baking powder thoroughly. Add this mixture in a layer on top of the egg.

Add the vinegar to the boiling water and fold into the rest of the ingredients using a fork, making sure the egg gets worked into the batter without overworking it. Pop into the microwave on high for 2½–3 minutes. It should feel dry and spongy.

Cool for 2 minutes, then flake the muffin-like cake to form smaller chunks. Gently cut through it with a fork to fluff up the chunks.

For the *smoor*, place the butter in a saucepan on medium heat and sauté the onions until soft. Add the can of tomato and onion mix. (If you don't reside in South Africa, just sauté 2 extra finely chopped onions and add a can of Italian-style peeled tomatoes in sauce.) Add the rest of the ingredients and allow to simmer and reduce for 5–8 minutes.

Cook the *wors* and then serve it with the *pap* and spoon over plenty of *smoor*. (The *pap* can also be used for any stew or dish that needs something to soak up the sauce.)

Yields 4 side servings at 12.5 g carbs per serving.

Pickled fish

5 Tbsp coconut oil
800 g hake fillet portions
Salt and pepper
2 large onions, sliced
1 Tbsp mild curry powder
2½ tsp turmeric
1 tsp ground ginger
3 bay leaves
¾ tsp ground coriander
1½ cups apple cider vinegar
1½ cups water
5 Tbsp xylitol
1 tsp stevia (optional)

Preheat the oven to 180 °C. Place the coconut oil in an ovenproof dish and place in the oven for a few minutes in order to melt the oil.

Lightly season the hake pieces with salt and pepper before placing them in the oil in the dish. Cover and bake for 15–20 minutes, turning the fish after 8–10 minutes. Cut the fish fillets into smaller portions. Make sure to remove all the skin.

Heat a little more coconut oil in a pan or saucepan, add the onions and fry until they start to soften. Add the curry powder, turmeric, ginger, bay leaves and coriander and stir through. Add the vinegar and water and bring to a simmer. Stir in the xylitol and stevia and season to taste. Simmer gently, while stirring, until the sauce has reduced and thickened slightly. Remove from heat and allow to cool.

Pack the fish fillets in an airtight container and cover with the sauce. Allow to marinate in the fridge for at least 24 hours before serving.

Yields 4 servings at 10 g carbs per serving.

Boerewors shepherd's pie

MY PICKY EATERS LOVE THIS ONE! BOEREWORS IS A VERY LONG SAUSAGE FILLED WITH BEEF, BACON FAT AND SPICES SUCH AS CORIANDER AND BLACK PEPPER, BUT YOU CAN USE ANY GOOD-QUALITY (CEREAL- AND DEXTROSE-FREE) SAUSAGE OR EVEN BEEF MINCE.

800 g–1 kg of your favourite boerewors, divided into 2 sausage wheels
5–6 cups cubed pumpkin
2 Tbsp butter
1 tsp ground cinnamon
½ tsp mixed spice
Sprinkle of ground cloves
1 head cauliflower, cut into florets
4 medium baby marrows, diced
½ cup fresh cream
1 x 410 g can chopped tomatoes
Salt and pepper to taste
1 Tbsp xylitol or a few drops of stevia (optional)
1 cup grated Cheddar cheese

Preheat the oven to 190 °C.

Cook the boerewors wheels in a pan with a little water. Keep the 2 wheels intact. (I put my 2 wheels on top of one another, add a bit more water and cover with a lid. The sausage does not have to be cooked all the way through, just mostly steamed through.)

Cook the pumpkin in a little salted water until soft and mashable. Add 1 Tbsp butter and the cinnamon, mixed spice and cloves and mash until creamy. (I cook my pumpkin with the skin on, because we like it and actually need that extra fibre, but the choice is yours.)

In a separate saucepan, cook the cauliflower florets and baby marrows in a little salted water until tender. Strain and mash with the remaining 1 Tbsp butter and the cream. Return to the heat and simmer on low for a minute or two.

In another saucepan, heat the canned tomatoes and add salt and pepper to taste. Sweeten with the xylitol or stevia.

To assemble, start with a layer of the tightly wound up boerewors. Scoop all the pumpkin mash onto the boerewors and layer all the tomato mix on the pumpkin. Now add the second boerewors wheel and layer all of the cauli–marrow mash on top of that. Lastly, sprinkle the grated cheese over the top and bake for 10–15 minutes until the cheese is golden brown.

Yields 6 servings at 13 g carbs per serving.

Curry marinade for sosaties

THIS MARINADE IS SWEET AND TANGY, YET 100 PER CENT LOW CARB.

2 Tbsp coconut oil
2 medium onions, finely chopped
2 Tbsp crushed garlic
2 Tbsp mild curry powder
1 cup brown vinegar
2 cups water
5 Tbsp xylitol
2 bay leaves
1 Tbsp turmeric
Salt and pepper
1 tsp ground cinnamon
¼ tsp ground ginger
2 medium onions, quartered

Heat the coconut oil in a saucepan on medium heat and sauté the finely chopped onions until soft. Add the garlic and curry powder and sauté for another minute. Add the rest of the ingredients, including the quartered onions, and gently simmer on low for 5 minutes.

Remove from heat and allow the marinade to cool completely before pouring over the meat of your choice (see options below). Allow the meat to soak in the marinade in the refrigerator for 24–36 hours before you thread it onto skewers along with the quartered onions and some cubed green, yellow and red peppers.

Yields enough sauce to marinate 1.5 kg meat cubes of choice, at about 3 g carbs per sosatie.

IDEAL CUTS OF MEAT FOR MAKING SOSATIES:
1.5 kg brisket or stewing beef
1.5 kg leg of lamb, deboned and cubed (don't trim any fat)
1.5 kg pork roast, deboned and cubed (don't trim any fat)
1.5 kg free-range chicken breasts, skin on

Lamb rib
Marinate a lovely lamb rib in the curry marinade for 24 hours. Remove from the marinade and throw over hot coals. The juicy chargrilled awesomeness will remind you of your BLCD (before low carb days), but this one hits the spot without the spike.

Count about 3 g carbs from the marinade per rib portion.

LEKKER TIPS

- You can make a bunch of sosaties at once and freeze them in family-sized portions.
- If you can get a hold of grass-fed meats, it is always ideal. Otherwise look for thicker, fatty cuts that you can cut from the bones and then cube. The bones can be used to make bone broth.

BBQ pork ribs

1–2 kg plain (not smoked) pork spareribs

1–2 cups Smoky BBQ Basting Sauce (p. 140)

Parboil the ribs in salted water for about 15–20 minutes.

Lay the ribs flat in a roasting pan and drench in basting sauce. Turn over a few times to make sure it is covered properly.

Now you can either hand it over to the braai master or you can pop it under a preheated oven grill. Turn and baste both sides at least twice.

Count about 3 g carbs from the marinade per rib portion.

Gourmet *Paptert* (porridge tart)

USUALLY MADE FROM MAIZE MEAL AND CORN, IT IS NOW 'DECARBED' AND BACK ON THE MENU.

PAP

1 large head cauliflower, cut into florets
3 Tbsp butter
1 Tbsp psyllium husks
1 cup nut meal (almond or pecan made in your grinder)
1 cup fresh cream
Salt and pepper to taste

SAUCE

2 Tbsp butter or coconut oil
1 cup sliced onions
1 x 410 g can chopped tomatoes
1 Tbsp white vinegar
1 Tbsp xylitol
1 tsp crushed garlic
1 tsp dried mixed herbs
Salt and pepper

TOPPING

1 x 250 g packet bacon bits
1½ cups grated Cheddar cheese

Preheat the oven grill.

For the *pap*, place the cauliflower florets in a food processor or blender and blend into couscous-sized pieces. Add the butter to a heavy-bottomed saucepan on medium heat and sauté the cauliflower for a few minutes. It should stay grainy in texture and not go mushy.

Dissolve the psyllium husks and nut meal in the cream and gently stir into the cauliflower. Season to taste. Turn the heat to low, place the lid on the saucepan and steam the mixture for a minute or two. When the mixture has a sticky, porridge-like texture, scoop it into a buttered ovenproof dish and spread evenly.

For the sauce, heat the butter or coconut oil in a saucepan on medium heat and sauté the onions. Add the rest of the sauce ingredients and simmer for 4–5 minutes until reduced a bit. Spread over the *pap* layer.

For the topping, fry the bacon bits in coconut oil until crisp. Sprinkle the bacon over the sauce, then sprinkle the cheese over the bacon. Place under the preheated grill until the cheese has melted and is golden brown.

Yields 6 main servings at 10.5 g carbs per serving or 10 side servings at 6.5 g carbs per serving.

Cheesy mushrooms

4 Tbsp butter
4 giant mushrooms
4 tsp crushed garlic
Salt and black pepper
1 tsp dried mixed herbs
4 slices salami
3 medium tomatoes, each cut into 4 slices
1 cup grated cheese of your choice

Cut 8 pieces of foil into the size of an A4 page.

On a double layer of foil, place ½ Tbsp of butter in the centre. Place a mushroom on top and trim the stem level with the flesh. Top the mushroom with another ½ Tbsp of butter, some garlic, salt, pepper and a sprinkling of herbs. Cover with a slice of salami, 3 slices of tomato and some grated cheese.

Pull up the two longer sides of foil and roll and pinch to create a steam bag. Repeat with the rest of the foil and ingredients.

Place on the braai grill and, depending on the heat of the fire and the distance from the grill, cook for 10–15 minutes until the cheese is oozy and the mushrooms are cooked.

Yields 4 main servings at 4.5 g carbs per serving or 8 side servings at 2–3 g carbs per serving.

Garlic brinjals

2 large brinjals, cut into 2 cm discs
2 tsp crushed garlic
½ cup melted butter
Salt and pepper to taste

Sprinkle the brinjal discs with salt and allow excess liquids to drain. Rinse and dry with a clean dish towel.

Add the garlic to the melted butter. Brush the garlic butter onto both sides of the brinjal and grill each side for a few minutes. Repeat with another coat or three of butter until it is nicely char-grilled. The brinjal should be grilled on the outside and buttery soft on the inside.

Yields 2 main servings at 5 g carbs per serving or 4 side servings at 2.5 g carbs per serving.

Braai toasties

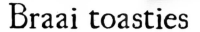

2 quantities Coconut and Flax Bread recipe (p. 151)

Follow and bake according to the recipe instructions.

Add butter, cheese, tomato, onion, salt and pepper to taste and hand over to the braai master!

Yields 16–18 slices at 3.75 g carbs per 2 slices. Add about 2 g carbs for the onion, tomato and cheese filling.

Biltong, mushroom and cauli casserole

1 head cauliflower, cut into florets
½ cup water
1 x 250 g punnet mushrooms of choice (I used a locally grown wild mix)
5 Tbsp butter
1 bunch spring onions, chopped
1 Tbsp crushed garlic
Salt and pepper to taste
1 cup fresh cream
1½ cups grated Cheddar cheese
½ cup cream cheese
1 handful fairly wet, fatty biltong (or spiced, cooked steak strips)
Nutmeg to taste

To prepare over a fire

Place the cauliflower florets and water in a cast-iron pot (*potjie*) and allow to steam for 5 minutes. As soon as the water has evaporated, add the mushrooms, butter, spring onions, garlic and seasoning. Sauté and stir until the cauliflower is tender.

In a jug, mix the cream, 1 cup grated cheese and the cream cheese together and pour into the pot. Allow to simmer and reduce gently. Add the biltong and stir gently through the veggies. Sprinkle the last bit of cheese on top, add a dusting of nutmeg, cover with the lid and remove from the direct coals. Set aside for a few minutes before serving.

To prepare in the oven

Preheat the oven to 180 °C. Steam the cauliflower florets. Heat the butter in a pan and sauté the mushrooms, spring onions and garlic. Blend 1 cup of grated cheese, the cream cheese, cream and seasoning together.

Drain the cauliflower and stir it into the creamed cheese mixture. Add the mushroom mixture and biltong. Gently stir through and pour into a casserole dish. Sprinkle cheese over the top and add some nutmeg. Bake for 20–25 minutes.

Yields 4–6 side servings (4 servings = 9 g carbs per serving, 6 servings = 6 g carbs per serving).

Baby marrow and cauli mash

Sides

Spinach and cauli mash

1 head cauliflower, cut into florets
1 x 300 g packet baby spinach
3 Tbsp butter
Salt and black pepper

Steam the cauliflower in a little water until tender. Add the spinach and steam with the cauliflower for about 5 minutes. Drain the excess water. Add the butter and seasoning and mash until smooth.

Yields 4 side servings at 3.5 g carbs per serving.

Baby marrow and cauli mash

1 head cauliflower, cut into florets
6–8 baby marrows, sliced
3 Tbsp butter
Salt and black pepper

Steam the cauliflower in a little water until tender. Add the baby marrows and steam with the cauliflower for 5–6 minutes. Drain the excess water. Add the butter and seasoning and mash until smooth.

Yields 4 side servings at 3.75 g carbs per serving.

Fried cabbage strips

3 Tbsp butter
½ head cabbage, shredded roughly into strips
¼ tsp crushed garlic (optional)
Salt or mixed herb salt and black pepper

Heat the butter in a pan on high heat and sauté the cabbage and garlic until the cabbage caramelises. Add the seasoning.

If you want to use this as a replacement for pasta, serve it crunchy. Cook a bit longer if you want to serve it as a side dish. You can also add crisply fried bacon bits to jazz it up and give a smoky flavour.

Yields 4 side servings at 2 g carbs per serving.

Stuffed mini peppers

YOU CAN SERVE THESE RAW OR COOKED, AND USE YOUR PREFERENCE AS FAR AS FILLINGS GO.

Baby sweet peppers (2–3 per person per portion)
Feta cheese
Pitted olives
Fresh basil leaves
Red spring onions
Coconut oil for frying

Cut a 'lid' off the top of the peppers and stuff the peppers with the feta cheese, olives and basil leaves. Heat a little coconut oil in a griddle pan and add the peppers and the whole spring onions. Char-grill them on high heat for 5–7 minutes, turning them every so often. They are ready when the filling starts to melt and the peppers are nicely charred all round.

Count 6 g carbs per 2–3 stuffed mini peppers.

Brinjal bocconcini bake

2 large brinjals, sliced into 5-mm-thick rounds
1 x 250 g packet streaky bacon or Parma ham strips
1 x 150 g tub bocconcini (mozzarella balls) or 1 cup grated mozzarella cheese
Pitted olives (optional)
2 spring onions, sliced
½ yellow pepper, cut into strips
Crushed garlic to taste
1 x 410 g can chopped tomatoes in juice
Mixed herbal salt and/or 1 Tbsp chopped mixed fresh herbs
Black pepper to taste
Grated Parmesan cheese

Preheat the oven to 190 °C.

Salt the brinjal rounds and let them drain for about 30 minutes.

Rinse the brinjal rounds and pat dry. Place them on a baking tray and bake for 20 minutes, turning at least once. Remove from oven and pack them like taco shells into 2 loaf pans.

Stuff each brinjal 'taco' with bacon, bocconcini, olives, spring onions, yellow pepper and garlic. Dress them with the canned tomatoes and season with herb salt and pepper.

Sprinkle over the Parmesan and fresh herbs and bake at 180 °C for 20–30 minutes. Drain off any excess liquid and serve immediately.

Yields 6 servings at 6 g carbs per serving.

Green bean bundles with mustard cream sauce

1 x 400 g packet fresh young green beans
1 Tbsp coconut oil
½ yellow pepper, cut into strips
3 red spring onions, cut into strips
1 tsp crushed garlic
Salt and black pepper or a grind of your favourite herbal salt mix
8–12 Parma or Black Forest ham strips
1 quantity Mustard Cream Sauce (p. 143)

For the bundles, first trim and clean the beans.

Heat the coconut oil in a pan on medium heat and sauté the beans, yellow pepper and spring onion strips for 3–4 minutes. Add the garlic and seasoning and cook for another 2–3 minutes. Allow the veggies to cool before dividing them into little bundles and wrapping them tightly with the ham.

Pack the bundles onto a serving platter.

Make the sauce as per the recipe instructions, adding any bits of garlic left behind from the pan in which you sautéed the veggies. Remove from heat and pour into a small serving dish with a spoon. Drizzle the sauce over the ham part of the green bean bundles.

Yields 8–10 bundles at 3–4 g carbs per serving, including sauce.

Creamy pumpkin and baby marrow bake

Creamy pumpkin and baby marrow bake

1 x 400 g packet pumpkin pieces or slices (ready prepared and available in the fresh produce aisle)
6 baby marrows, sliced
3 Tbsp butter
½ cup fresh cream
1 tsp ground cinnamon
1 Tbsp xylitol
Salt and pepper

Preheat the oven to 180 °C.

Layer the pumpkin and baby marrows in an ovenproof dish. Dot butter evenly over the veggies. Pour over the cream and sprinkle with the cinnamon and xylitol. Season to taste. Bake for 25–30 minutes until the pumpkin is soft and browned and has a caramel-like sauce.

Yields 4 servings at 7.5 g carbs per serving.

Green bean casserole

2 Tbsp coconut oil or lard
1 large onion, thinly sliced
1 Tbsp grated Parmesan cheese (optional)
2 cups sliced green beans
4 yellow patty pans, sliced
1 x 250 g punnet mushrooms, sliced
¼ red pepper, finely diced
2 tsp crushed garlic
Salt to taste
½ tsp ground black pepper
1 Tbsp grated lemon zest
2 Tbsp lemon juice
1 Tbsp butter
1 cup fresh cream

Heat the coconut oil in saucepan on medium–high heat and fry the onion until very crispy. Sprinkle with the Parmesan or just a pinch of salt, and scoop into a separate dish. Set aside.

Using the same saucepan in which you fried the onion, stir-fry the green beans, patty pans, mushrooms, red pepper and garlic. Season with salt and black pepper.

You can stop cooking at this point and just grate the lemon zest over the veggies and add the lemon juice before serving with the crunchy onions, or you can add the butter and cream and allow it to simmer and thicken for 5–7 minutes for the full experience.

Yields 4 servings at 8 g carbs per serving.

Broccoli with creamy lemon–butter sauce

1 head broccoli
1 quantity Creamy Lemon–Butter Sauce (p. 143)
Herbal salt and black pepper to taste

Steam the broccoli in a little salted water. The broccoli should be tender enough to easily cut the florets, but still have a bit of a crunch. Drain all excess water and cut into florets. Place them in your serving dish and drizzle liberally with the lemon butter sauce. Give a grind of mixed herbs and black pepper.

Yields 4–6 servings (4 servings = 4 g carbs per serving, 6 servings = 2.7 g carbs per serving).

Spicy pumpkin and brinjal bake

2 Tbsp coconut oil
1 x 400 g packet cubed pumpkin (ready prepared and available in the fresh produce aisle)
1 large brinjal, cubed
8 cauliflower florets, halved
½ red pepper, roughly chopped
½ yellow pepper, roughly chopped
1 x 400 ml can coconut cream
8 cherry tomatoes
Pumpkin seeds to garnish
1 satsuma orange, sliced into segments and/or fresh coriander leaves (optional)

SPICE MIX
1 tsp mild curry powder
½ tsp ground ginger
½ tsp ground cinnamon
¼ tsp ground cardamom (optional)
½ tsp turmeric
½ tsp crushed coriander seeds
1 Tbsp xylitol
1 Tbsp lemon juice
Salt and black pepper to taste

Preheat the oven to 180 °C.

Heat the coconut oil in a saucepan on high heat and sauté the pumpkin, brinjal, cauliflower and peppers until they start to caramelise on the edges.

Stir all the spice mix ingredients into the can of coconut cream. Mix well.

Place the fried veggies and spicy coconut cream together into a single casserole dish and bake for about 40 minutes. The pumpkin must be soft and the coconut cream fairly reduced. Add the cherry tomatoes and grill until nicely browned.

Scatter over some pumpkin seeds, squeeze the orange segments over the veggies and add some coriander leaves just before serving.

Yields 6 side servings at 8 g carbs per serving.

Pumpkin fritters

FRITTERS

1¼ cups cooked, mashed pumpkin
(very well drained)
1 Tbsp xylitol
2 large free-range eggs
1 cup nut flour (almond or pecan)
or pumpkin seed meal
2 tsp baking powder
Pinch salt
1 tsp psyllium husks
Sprinkle ground cinnamon
Coconut oil for frying

TO SERVE

A few small cubes of butter
2 Tbsp xylitol mixed with 1 tsp
ground cinnamon

Place the pumpkin, xylitol, eggs, nut flour, baking powder, salt, psyllium and cinnamon together in a bowl. Mix well.

In a pan on medium to high heat, melt 1 Tbsp coconut oil per batch of three or four fritters. Fry heaped tablespoonsful of batter until the edges form a brown crust and a few bubbles appear on top. Flipping these fritters needs to happen swiftly. If you can easily scoop up the little fellow, then the bottom is cooked enough, otherwise allow another few seconds and rather turn down the heat a bit. Flip and fry for about a minute on the other side.

Dish onto a serving platter, place a cube of butter in the centre of each fritter and sprinkle with a bit of the cinnamon mix. Repeat with the rest of the batter.

Yields 8–10 fritters at 3–4 g carbs per fritter.

LEKKER TIPS

- For a very decadent variation, make the Quick Caramel Syrup on p. 180 and drizzle over the fritters before serving.

Condiments
and Sauces

Mexican spice

1½ tsp chilli flakes
2 Tbsp paprika
1½ tsp dried oregano
4½ tsp ground cumin
2 tsp salt
1½ tsp fine black pepper
½ tsp ground cinnamon
½ tsp ground cloves
2 tsp garlic flakes

Mix everything together and store in an airtight container for up to 3 months. Add a few teaspoons to minced beef or a chicken sandwich filling to put the 'olé!' back into your day.

Moroccan spice

2 tsp ground ginger
2 tsp ground cardamom
1 tsp ground cinnamon
1 tsp ground allspice or mixed spice
1 tsp ground coriander
1 tsp ground nutmeg
1 tsp turmeric
½ tsp ground black pepper
½ tsp ground white pepper
½ tsp cayenne pepper
½ tsp ground aniseed seeds

Mix everything together and store in an airtight container for up to 3 months. Add a few teaspoons to chicken, beef or lamb stews.

Berry jam

1½ cups frozen or fresh
mixed berries
½ cup water
4 Tbsp xylitol
¼ tsp fine psyllium husks (optional)

Simmer the berries, water and xylitol in a saucepan on medium heat for 15–20 minutes, until reduced and thickened. Remove from heat and stir in the psyllium husks, if using. That's it!

Yields ³/₄ cup jam at 1.5 g carbs per 1 Tbsp serving.

Cherry tomato and ginger jam

2 Tbsp coconut oil
400 g cherry tomatoes
3 Tbsp xylitol
1 tsp chilli flakes
1 Tbsp ginger flakes or grated
fresh ginger
1 tsp fine black pepper
¼ tsp salt

Melt the coconut oil in a medium saucepan on medium heat.

Add the tomatoes and the rest of the ingredients. Stir just enough to coat the tomatoes with the spices. Simmer, without stirring, for 5–7 minutes, until the tomatoes start to ooze in the fragrant syrup. DO NOT STIR. The tomatoes need to stay as whole as possible.

As soon as the syrup reduces to a thicker and darker brown colour, remove from heat and put the lid on the saucepan to retain the heat. Allow to cool to room temperature.

Scoop some freshly made jam over a beautiful Brie or Camembert or simply store in a covered glass jar in the refrigerator.

The entire quantity of jam is 19 g carbs, which translates to 1.2 g carbs per 1 Tbsp serving.

LEKKER TIPS

- Enjoy on scrambled eggs or in a low-carb Breakfast Wrap (p. 45).

Tomato sauce

1 x 410 g can tomato purée
2 Tbsp white vinegar
¼ tsp fine white pepper
1 tsp salt
¼ tsp finely crushed garlic
2 Tbsp xylitol
¼ tsp psyllium husks

Place all the ingredients, except the psyllium husks, in a saucepan on medium heat. Allow to gently simmer and reduce for 15 minutes.

Stir in the psyllium husks and remove from heat. Allow to cool, then store in a covered glass jar in the refrigerator. It will keep for 7–10 days.

Yields about 1¹/₂ cups at less than 1 g carbs per 1 Tbsp serving.

Cherry tomato and ginger jam

Spicy chutney

Creamy mayo

3 egg yolks
¼ tsp salt
¼ tsp mustard powder
¾ cup melted coconut oil or light olive oil
2 tsp xylitol
2 Tbsp white vinegar
½ cup sour cream

Using a stick blender, blend the egg yolks, salt and mustard powder together. Slowly add the oil and xylitol while blending. Now add the vinegar and mix well. Lastly, add the sour cream and whisk to a well-combined, light consistency. Store in a covered glass jar in the refrigerator. It will keep for 7–10 days.

Yields around 1½ cups at 8.8 g carbs for the batch, or 0.4 g carbs per 1 Tbsp serving.

LEKKER TIPS

- Add a little low-carb Tomato sauce (p.136) to make a pink sauce, which kids love!

Spicy chutney

4 Tbsp coconut oil
3 medium onions, finely chopped
1 red pepper, finely chopped
1 yellow pepper, finely chopped
1 small apple, finely chopped
2 Tbsp xylitol
1 Tbsp turmeric
1 Tbsp mild curry powder
2 tsp ground ginger
½ tsp paprika
½ tsp ground cumin
1 Tbsp crushed garlic
1 cup water
2 Tbsp apple cider vinegar
1 Tbsp tomato purée
Salt and pepper to taste

Heat the oil in a saucepan on medium–high heat and sauté the onions, peppers and apple until soft.

Stir in the rest of the ingredients and allow to simmer on low to medium heat for 8–10 minutes until the chutney reduces to a thicker consistency. (You might have to top up the water a bit during this process.) Remove from heat and cool. Store in a covered glass jar in the refrigerator. It will keep for 7–10 days.

Yields almost 1½ cups at around 1.8 g carbs per 1 Tbsp serving.

Easy tzatziki

¾ cup double-cream yoghurt
Salt and black pepper
⅓ English cucumber, seeds removed and flesh grated
1 Tbsp chopped fresh mint
1 tsp crushed garlic

Mix all the ingredients together and refrigerate until needed.

Yields 8 servings at 2 g carbs per serving.

Smoky BBQ basting sauce

4 Tbsp coconut oil
1 onion, finely chopped
2 Tbsp crushed garlic
1 Tbsp dried mixed herbs
2 tsp smoked salt (regular will work too)
2 Tbsp ground coriander
2 Tbsp crushed coriander seeds
1 tsp ground cloves
1 Tbsp fine black pepper
1 Tbsp paprika
½ tsp chilli flakes
4 Tbsp xylitol
4 Tbsp apple cider vinegar
Squeeze of lemon juice
1 x 410 g can tomato purée
1 Tbsp Dijon mustard
½ cup water

Heat the coconut oil in a medium saucepan on medium heat and caramelise the onion with the garlic, herbs and salt.

Add all the spices and allow to infuse for about 1 minute. Now add all the remaining ingredients and simmer for 5 minutes. Remove from heat. Quickly run a stick blender through the sauce. Allow to cool and apply generous amounts to pork ribs, chicken wings, pork chops, and so on.

Store in a covered glass jar in the refrigerator. It will keep for 7–10 days. Alternatively, freeze what you don't need and defrost at room temperature before using. Always pour the amount you need into a smaller bowl to avoid cross-contamination.

Add about 10 g carbs per 100 g basting sauce you use on your preferred meat cuts.

Fragrant basting sauce

3 Tbsp butter
2 Tbsp lemon juice
2 tsp crushed garlic
1 tsp curry powder
1 Tbsp chopped fresh mixed herbs or 1 tsp dried
1 tsp xylitol (optional)
4 Tbsp plain double-cream yoghurt, amasi or coconut milk
½ tsp Dijon mustard
Salt and pepper to taste

Melt the butter in a saucepan on low heat and add the rest of the ingredients. Allow the flavours to infuse for a minute or two.

Remove from heat and allow marinade to cool. Pour over chicken pieces and bake in the sauce or brush onto chicken wings, pork chops or steak and grill or fry. This basting sauce must be used immediately.

Add about 10 g carbs to whichever dish you add this to.

Smoky BBQ basting sauce

Old-fashioned sweet mustard sauce

JUST LIKE GRANDMA'S, BUT WITHOUT THE CONDENSED MILK!

2 extra-large eggs
4 Tbsp xylitol
¼ tsp salt
½ cup white vinegar
1 heaped tsp mustard powder
1 Tbsp Dijon mustard
1 Tbsp butter
½ cup Creamy Mayo (p. 139) or fresh cream

Using an electric mixer, beat the eggs and gradually add the xylitol until the mixture is light and fluffy. Add salt and then gradually add the vinegar while mixing well.

Place the mixture in a double boiler (or heatproof bowl suspended over a saucepan of simmering water) and whisk until it starts to heat up and thicken. Add the mustards and butter and mix well. Once thick and custardy, remove from heat and whisk in the mayonnaise or cream. Allow mustard to cool before serving. It will keep for 7–10 days in a covered glass jar in the refrigerator.

Yields just over 1 cup at about 1.5 g carbs per 1 Tbsp serving.

LEKKER TIPS

- Make a cold 'decarbed potato salad' using steamed cauliflower, 4 Tbsp Old-fashioned Sweet Mustard Sauce and ½ cup Creamy Mayo (p. 139), and add slices of boiled egg.

Mushroom sauce

Knob of butter or coconut oil
1 x 250 g punnet mushrooms, sliced
Salt and black pepper to taste
1 tsp crushed garlic
1 cup fresh cream
½ cup grated Cheddar cheese

Heat the butter in a saucepan on medium heat and sauté the mushrooms for about 5 minutes. Add the seasoning and garlic and sauté for 1 minute. Add the cream and cheese. Simmer and reduce on low heat, stirring often, for 5–8 minutes. Serve hot.

Yields 4–6 servings (4 servings = 3.5 g carbs per serving, 6 servings = 2.3 g carbs per serving).

Cheese sauce

4 Tbsp butter
1 cup fresh cream
1 cup grated mature Cheddar cheese
Sprinkle of nutmeg (optional)

Melt the butter in a saucepan on medium heat. Stir in the cream and add the cheese. Whisk continuously until the cheese melts. Allow the sauce to simmer gently and thicken on low heat for 10–12 minutes. Keep whisking. The sauce is ready when it has large bubbles and has reduced by almost half. Sprinkle with nutmeg and serve.

Yields 1 cup sauce, enough for 6–8 servings of meat, fish or veggies, at 1 g carbs per serving.

Pepper sauce

4 Tbsp butter
1 Tbsp whole peppercorns, crushed in a coffee grinder or with a pestle and mortar (you can use black or a mix of black, red and green peppercorns)
½ tsp crushed garlic
Salt to taste
1 cup fresh cream
½ cup beef stock
2 Tbsp Cognac or brandy (optional)

Melt the butter in a saucepan on medium heat. Add the peppercorns, garlic and salt. Pour in the cream and stock and allow the sauce to simmer on medium heat for 10–12 minutes until reduced to a creamy consistency. Whisk constantly for the duration of the cooking time. Stir in the Cognac or brandy a few minutes before you are ready to remove the saucepan from the heat.

Yields just over 1 cup sauce, enough for 6–8 servings of meat, at 1 g carbs per serving.

LEKKER TIPS

- **Emergency stock:** Make a quick stock by trimming off a piece of the meat you are planning to prepare, add 2 baby carrots, ½ celery stick and leaves, 1 slice onion and a sprinkling of salt and pepper. Add 1–2 cups water and boil while you prepare your veggies etc. This does not have the same health benefits of a good bone broth, but it works well in the taste department.

Mustard cream sauce

3 Tbsp butter
1 Tbsp Dijon mustard
1 cup fresh cream
Salt to taste
1 tsp xylitol
Grind of black pepper
Squeeze of lemon juice

Melt the butter in a saucepan on medium heat. Add the rest of the ingredients and simmer on medium heat for 2–3 minutes until reduced to a creamy consistency.

Yields just over 1 cup sauce, enough for 4–6 servings of meat (4 servings = 2.2 g carbs per serving, 6 servings = 1.5 g carbs per serving).

Creamy lemon–butter sauce

4 Tbsp butter
1 cup fresh cream
1 Tbsp chopped fresh parsley or dill
4 Tbsp lemon juice
Salt and pepper to taste

Melt the butter in a saucepan on medium heat. Add the cream, herbs and lemon juice and allow the sauce to simmer on medium heat for 6–8 minutes until creamy and reduced by a third. Season to taste.

Yields just over 1 cup sauce, enough for 6–8 servings of meat, fish or veggies, at 1.3–1.8 g carbs per serving.

Blackberry vinaigrette

1 cup frozen blackberries
2 Tbsp vinegar or lemon juice
½ tsp fresh thyme leaves
Salt and pepper to taste
3 Tbsp + 1 tsp olive oil
3 Tbsp + 1 tsp water
1 tsp each xylitol and lemon zest
¼ tsp ground ginger

Thaw the berries and heat for a minute or two in a saucepan on low heat to extract the juice.

Remove from heat, add the rest of the ingredients and blend to form a light vinaigrette. Allow to cool and store in a covered glass jar in the refrigerator for up to a week. Pour over your favourite salad.

Yields about 1 cup or 8 servings at 1.2 g carbs per serving.

Pre- and pro-biotic salad dressing

1 cup amasi (pro-biotic booster)
4 Tbsp olive oil
A few grinds of Himalayan salt
2 Tbsp white vinegar
1 Tbsp crushed garlic (17.5 % pre-biotic fibre)
½ baby leek (11.7% pre-biotic fibre)
½ small onion, finely diced (8.6% pre-biotic fibre)
4 asparagus spears, finely chopped (5% pre-biotic fibre)
Black pepper to taste
4 Tbsp fresh coriander leaves
Squeeze of lemon juice

Blend all the ingredients together using a stick blender or food processor. Scoop over your favourite leafy green salad or roast veg salad. Refrigerate for a few days only.

Yields just over 1½ cups or 12 servings at 1.5 g carbs per serving.

Poppy, lime and ginger dressing

¾ cup coconut milk
2 Tbsp olive oil
3 Tbsp white vinegar
1 tsp crushed garlic
1 Tbsp freshly minced ginger
1 Tbsp poppy seeds
1 Tbsp toasted sesame seeds
1 tsp Dijon mustard
Juice of ½ lime and zest of 1 lime
Salt and pepper to taste
1 tsp xylitol (optional)

Blend all the ingredients together and smother the first chicken salad that dares to come your way! Or refrigerate until such a time of awesomeness arrives. This dressing keeps well in the refrigerator for up to a week.

Yields about 1 cup or 8 servings at about 2 g carbs per serving.

Creamy black pepper, feta and herb dressing

½ cup sour cream
1½ rounds of feta cheese
A few good grinds of black pepper
Salt
4 Tbsp apple cider vinegar
2 Tbsp olive oil
½ tsp crushed garlic
1 tsp dried thyme or mixed herbs
1 tsp xylitol (optional)
4–5 Tbsp water

Blend all the ingredients together using a stick blender or food processor. Scoop over your favourite leafy green salad, cabbage slaw or Bacon, Broccoli and Red Cabbage Salad (p. 63). Refrigerate for up to a week.

Yields about 1 cup or 8 servings at 2 g carbs per serving.

Breads, Rolls and Pizza

Basic bread recipe 1

SPECIAL CREDIT TO MARIA EMMERICH AND HER STUNNING BLOG (HTTP://MARIAMINDBODYHEALTH.COM), WHICH SPURRED ON A WHOLE NEW LOW-CARB BREAD SCIENCE FOR ME.

1½ cups almond meal or flour
½ cup flax meal (golden flaxseed will give this bread a lighter colour)
2 heaped Tbsp fine desiccated coconut
5 Tbsp psyllium husk fibre (this ingredient is important)
2 tsp baking powder
½ tsp salt
4 free-range egg whites
2½ Tbsp apple cider vinegar
1 cup boiling water

Basic bread recipe 2 (Budget-smart option)

THE PUMPKIN SEED MEAL GIVES THIS BREAD AN ALMOST-WHOLEWHEAT TEXTURE, WHICH IS LOVELY AND VERY TASTY.

1½ cups pumpkin seed meal
½ cup golden or brown flax meal
2 heaped Tbsp fine desiccated coconut
5 Tbsp psyllium husk fibre (this ingredient is important)
2 tsp baking powder
½ tsp salt
2½ Tbsp apple cider vinegar
4 free-range egg whites
1 cup boiling water

Preheat the oven to 180 °C.

Place all the dry ingredients in a mixing bowl. Mix with a fork to make sure the psyllium powder is well mixed into the rest of the flours.

Give the egg whites a quick whisk and add the vinegar. Pour the egg mixture into the dry ingredients and mix well. Now add the hot water. Stir quickly to form a 'puffy' batter.

It is important that you DON'T let this batter sit too long before baking. Try to form it into the desired shape and get it into the oven within 3 minutes for the best results.

Very gently shape the dough into loaves or rolls in order to preserve the puffy texture. The batter will at the least double in size during baking so keep this in mind when spacing.

The entire batter for Basic Bread Recipe 1 amounts to 25 g carbs. The entire batter for Basic Bread Recipe 2 amounts to 29 g carbs. Simply divide into portions to get a per portion carb count.

Rustic bread

Simply shape the dough into a ball and bake on a buttered baking tray for 50–55 minutes. Switch off the oven and leave the bread inside for another 10 minutes before transferring to a wire rack to cool.

Sandwich loaf

Shape the batter into a sausage and place into a buttered loaf pan. Bake for 50–55 minutes. Switch off the oven and leave the bread inside for another 10 minutes before transferring to a wire rack to cool. Best served while still crusty. This loaf can be sliced and used for toast, toasted cheese pan sandwiches and braai toasties. Store in an airtight container for 2–3 days, or freeze in portions and thaw at room temperature.

Burger buns

Divide and shape the batter into 5 or 6 equal balls. Place on a buttered baking tray and bake for 40 minutes. Switch off the oven and leave the buns inside for another 10 minutes before transferring to a wire rack to cool. Cool and serve within a few hours for a crusty bun or a soft bun.

Hot dog buns

Divide the batter into 5 or 6 equal parts and gently roll to form a sausage shape. Place on a buttered baking tray and bake for 35–40 minutes. Switch off the oven and leave the buns inside for another 10 minutes before transferring to a wire rack to cool. Cool and serve while still crusty.

Garlic loaf

Roll the batter into a long French loaf shape and place across the length of a buttered baking tray. Bake for 45–50 minutes. Switch off the oven and leave the loaf inside for another 10 minutes before transferring to a wire rack to cool. When cool, place on a sheet of foil and slice into sections, but not all the way through. Spread each section with garlic butter. Stuff with mozzarella cheese and wrap the foil sheet loosely over the loaf. Melt the cheese on the grill outside or in the oven at 180 °C for 8–10 minutes before serving.

Bread sticks

Divide the batter into 8 equal pieces and roll them into long, thin strips. Place across the width of a buttered baking tray and brush with garlic butter. Sprinkle with a herb grinder blend or some grated Parmesan and bake for 25–30 minutes. Cool and serve with a dip.

Pizza crust

Divide the dough half and roll out each half on a buttered baking tray. Bake for about 25 minutes or until it is brown and crusty. Spread a thin layer of tomato purée over the crust and add the toppings of your choice. Return to the oven until the cheese has melted.

Bread sticks

Coconut and flax bread

Nut meal and flax bread

1 cup pecan, almond or pumpkin seed meal
½ cup flaxseed
½ cup flax meal
3 Tbsp psyllium husk fibre
2 tsp baking powder
½ tsp bicarbonate of soda
1 Tbsp xylitol
½ tsp salt
2 large free-range eggs
2 Tbsp coconut oil or butter
¾ cup lukewarm water
2 Tbsp sesame seeds
2 Tbsp poppy seeds

Preheat the oven to 180 °C.

Mix all the dry ingredients together thoroughly in a mixing bowl.

Whisk the eggs and mix them into the dry ingredients. Let the oil or butter melt in the warm water and then pour this mixture into the dough. Mix properly and then let the dough rest for 2 minutes.

Scoop the dough into a buttered loaf pan and sprinkle with the seeds. Bake for 45–50 minutes.

Yields 1 loaf at 21 g carbs for the entire loaf. Simply divide into portions to get a per portion carb count.

Coconut and flax bread (no nuts bread)

DOUBLE THE BATTER FOR A BIGGER SANDWICH LOAF SUITABLE FOR THE BRAAI TOASTIES ON P. 123.

1 cup coconut meal
½ cup flaxseed
½ cup flax meal
3 Tbsp psyllium husk fibre
2 tsp baking powder
½ tsp bicarbonate of soda
1 Tbsp xylitol
½ tsp salt
3 large free-range eggs
2 Tbsp coconut oil or butter
¾ cup hot water
4 Tbsp mixed seeds

Preheat the oven to 180 °C.

Mix all the dry ingredients together thoroughly in a mixing bowl.

Whisk the eggs and mix into the flour. Let the oil or butter melt in the hot water and then pour the mixture into the dough. Mix properly and then let the dough rest for 2 minutes. Pour into a buttered loaf pan and sprinkle with the seeds. Bake for 45–50 minutes.

Yields 1 loaf at 15 g carbs for the entire loaf. Simply divide into portions to get a per portion carb count.

Four-seeds bread

THIS IS MY ALL-TIME FAVOURITE, WHICH I OFTEN SERVE STRAIGHT FROM THE OVEN WITH FARM BUTTER AND A BEAUTIFUL PLATTER. THIS BREAD HAS WON OVER THE HEARTS OF MANY LOW-CARB SCEPTICS!

1½ cups almond, pecan or pumpkin seed meal
½ cup flax meal
2 tsp baking powder
½ tsp salt
3 Tbsp psyllium husk fibre
4 Tbsp whole pumpkin seeds, plus extra 4 Tbsp for sprinkling on top
4 Tbsp whole flaxseed
4 Tbsp sunflower seeds, plus extra 4 Tbsp for sprinkling on top
4 Tbsp sesame seeds
3 free-range egg whites
1 Tbsp apple cider vinegar
1 cup hot water

Preheat the oven to 180 °C.

Mix all the dry ingredients and seeds together thoroughly in a mixing bowl.

Beat the egg whites and add the vinegar. Add this mixture to the dry ingredients and stir well. Mix in the hot water and then transfer the dough into a buttered loaf pan or make a lovely rustic bread by shaping the dough into a round or oval shape on a buttered baking tray. Cut a cross into the dough and sprinkle with the extra seeds. Bake for 55–60 minutes.

Yields 1 loaf at 40 g carbs for the entire loaf. Simply divide into portions to get a per portion carb count.

Cheese scones

THESE SCONES ARE WONDERFUL SERVED WITH SOUP.

¾ cup almond flour
½ cup flax meal
2 tsp baking powder
Pinch salt
6 Tbsp melted butter
6 Tbsp full-cream milk
2 free-range eggs
¾ cup grated Cheddar cheese

Preheat the oven to 180 °C.

Mix the almond flour, flax meal, baking powder and salt together in a mixing bowl.

In a separate mixing bowl, mix the melted butter, milk, eggs and cheese together. Add the wet to the dry ingredients. Don't overwork the batter. Fill 8 muffin holes of a silicone muffin tray to two-thirds full or use muffin cups and fill a regular pan. Bake for 15–20 minutes until firm and browned.

Yields 8 scones at 2.5 g carbs per scone.

Baby marrow and Cheddar röstis

½ cup flax meal
½ cup pumpkin seed meal
2 tsp baking powder
½ tsp salt
2 free-range eggs
1 cup grated Cheddar cheese
3 baby marrows, grated
Coconut oil for frying

Mix the flax meal, pumpkin seed meal, baking powder and salt together in a mixing bowl. Add the eggs, cheese and baby marrows and mix well. Melt some coconut oil in a pan on medium–high heat and scoop tablespoonsful of batter into the pan. Fry until brown and firm on the one side and then flip and fry the other side.

Yields 8–10 röstis at 3 g carbs per rösti.

Desserts

Malva pudding

PUDDING

2 Tbsp xylitol
1 Tbsp apricot diabetic jam (optional)
2 free-range eggs
1 cup ground almonds
½ cup fine desiccated coconut
1 tsp bicarbonate of soda
Pinch salt
2 Tbsp butter
1 Tbsp brown vinegar
½ cup full-cream milk

SAUCE

1 cup fresh cream
½ cup butter
2 Tbsp xylitol
4 Tbsp water

Preheat the oven to 190 °C.

For the pudding, beat the xylitol, jam and eggs together until fluffy and creamy. Mix the dry ingredients in a separate bowl.

Melt the butter in a small saucepan on medium heat. Add the vinegar and milk and stir. Remove from heat and add the milk mixture to the dry ingredients. Mix well.

Next, add the egg mixture and mix well using a whisk or wooden spoon. Pour into an ovenproof dish and bake for 25–30 minutes or until firm but spongy and nicely browned.

For the sauce, melt all the ingredients together in a small saucepan on medium to high heat. Allow to simmer for 2 minutes, stirring constantly so that it does not boil over. Pour the sauce over the pudding as soon as it comes out of the oven.

Serve with whipped cream or Vanilla Ice Cream (p. 165).

Yields 4–6 servings at 7–10 g carbs per serving.

Caramel and peppermint chocolate tartlets

CARAMEL FILLING
5 Tbsp butter
1 cup double cream
5 Tbsp xylitol
1 tsp vanilla extract
1–2 blocks mint dark chocolate

CRUST
2 Tbsp fine desiccated coconut (optional)
1 cup nut flour
1 Tbsp xylitol
1 Tbsp cocoa powder (optional)
2 Tbsp unsalted butter, at room temperature

TOPPING
½ cup fresh cream
1 block mint dark chocolate

For the caramel filling, melt the butter in a saucepan on medium to high heat. Add ½ cup of the cream and the xylitol and stir for 3 minutes. The mixture will bubble. Keep stirring to keep it from boiling over, and don't let it burn. After the sauce has browned, you can let it simmer while stirring continuously for another 3 minutes or so. (I vary my heat between medium and short spurts on high.)

When the sauce has thickened and has a nice gloss to the top layer, you can take it off the heat, add the vanilla and let it cool.

As soon as the caramel has cooled, add the remaining ½ cup of cream and whisk with a hand mixer until the mixture forms peaks. Grate the mint dark chocolate into the caramel cream and fold in.

For the crust, mix all the dry ingredients together in a mixing bowl and then rub in the butter. Divide into 10 portions and press onto the base of the holes in a small muffin tray (the silicone kind works best).

Scoop the caramel filling onto the prepared crusts, cover with plastic wrap and pop into the freezer for 20 minutes. (These guys can actually stay in the freezer and you can pop them out as needed, then top with whipped cream and grate some mint chocolate on top. Just make sure to keep them well covered with plastic wrap or foil.)

When ready to serve, whip the cream until thick. Pop out the minty tartlets and top with the whipped cream. Grate the chocolate block over the cream.

Yields 10 tartlets at about 5.5 g carbs per tartlet. (Compared to almost 50 g carbs for a regular slice of Peppermint Crisp tart, it's not too shabby. Low carb is lekker!)

Milk tart

CRUST

1 cup almond flour
2 Tbsp fine desiccated coconut
1 Tbsp xylitol
4 Tbsp melted butter

FILLING

2 cups fresh cream
Pinch salt
2 Tbsp xylitol
½ tsp stevia powder
4 free-range eggs, separated
2 Tbsp butter
1 tsp vanilla extract
1 tsp psyllium husk fibre
1–1½ tsp ground cinnamon

Preheat the oven to 180 °C.

For the crust, mix the flour, coconut and xylitol together in a mixing bowl. Pour over the melted butter and mix in. Press the dough onto the base of a buttered dinner plate-sized ovenproof dish. Alternatively, I would suggest you use 4 single-serving ramekins or 8–10 cupcake moulds.

For the filling, heat the cream, salt, xylitol and stevia in a heavy-bottomed saucepan on medium heat. Give the egg yolks a quick whisk and stir into the cream while it is still lukewarm. Stir constantly. As soon as the mixture starts to thicken, stir in the butter and vanilla and remove from heat.

Whisk the egg whites and psyllium for about 30 seconds until foamy and almost doubled in volume. Fold the egg white mixture into the custard mixture and then pour the custard filling over the crust. Sprinkle with cinnamon. Bake for 20–30 minutes or until the milk tart looks puffed up, slightly browned and set.

Yields 6–8 servings at 5–7 g carbs per serving.

Melkkos

IT IS BEST TO PREPARE THE *SNYSELS* (STRIPS OF DOUGH) BEFORE YOU MAKE THE CUSTARD.

SNYSELS
3 free-range eggs
½ x 230 g block cream cheese
3 Tbsp fine desiccated coconut
Tiny pinch salt
Coconut oil for frying

CUSTARD
2 cups fresh cream
1 cup full-cream milk
1 cup water
¼ tsp salt
1 Tbsp xylitol
6 free-range eggs, separated
2 tsp vanilla extract
2 Tbsp butter
¼ tsp psyllium husk fibre

SPRINKLES
3 Tbsp xylitol
1 tsp ground cinnamon

Mix all the *snysels* ingredients together in a mixing bowl and then blend with a stick blender. Pour a thin layer of the batter into a pan on high heat, much like you would when making make a pancake. As soon as the edges are hard and brown and you can manoeuvre the spatula easily under the pancake, flip and bake on the other side for a few seconds. Place the pancake on a plate and repeat until you have used up all the batter.

Roll up the pancakes and cut them into 1-cm-wide strips. These are now your *snysels*.

Start on the custard by warming the cream, milk, water, salt and xylitol in a heavy-bottomed saucepan on medium to high heat. Turn the heat to low just before the mix reaches boiling point.

Beat the egg yolks with a fork in a separate small bowl and scoop some lukewarm milk into the yolks. Mix well and then slowly add the yolk mixture to the milk mixture in the saucepan while stirring with a whisk. The sauce should start to thicken slightly after 4–5 minutes of stirring. As soon as the sauce starts to thicken, add the vanilla and the butter and whisk until well incorporated. Add the *snysels* and stir gently with a wooden spoon, making sure to keep the *snysels* mostly intact. Turn the heat back up to medium, cover the saucepan with a lid and allow to steam for a minute or two.

Add the psyllium husk fibre to the egg whites and whisk together until fairly stiff. Fold the egg whites into the custard and give the psyllium a chance to develop for a minute. Remove from heat and serve with a sprinkling of cinnamon and xylitol.

Yields 4–6 servings at a little less than 6 g carbs per serving.

Pancakes

PANCAKES

6 large free-range eggs

½ x 230 g block cream cheese

½ cup full-cream milk

½ tsp salt

2 Tbsp melted butter

1 Tbsp xylitol

½ tsp baking powder

½ cup almond meal

Coconut oil for frying

Slices of lemon

TOPPING

3 Tbsp xylitol

1 tsp ground cinnamon

Put all the pancake ingredients, except the coconut oil and lemon, in a mixing bowl and mix together using a stick blender.

Melt a small knob of coconut oil in a non-stick pan on high heat, swirling the pan so the oil covers the entire surface. The pan should be well heated before adding a ¼ cup of pancake batter. Swirl and cook until the edges turn brown and pull away from the pan. Quickly loosen all sides before flipping and cooking the other side of the pancake for 20–30 seconds.

Place the pancake on a warm plate and repeat with the rest of the batter.

Mix the topping ingredients and sprinkle over the pancakes. Roll up and serve.

Yields 10 pancakes at 4 g carbs per pancake.

 LEKKER TIPS

- The Breakfast Wrap recipe on p. 45 also makes for a great pancake when dressed with a sprinkle of xylitol and cinnamon.

Mousse

CHOCOLATE MOUSSE
1 cup fresh cream
2 Tbsp cocoa powder
1 Tbsp xylitol
1 tsp vanilla extract

BERRY MOUSSE
1 cup fresh cream
½ cup strawberry purée (about
1 cup whole fresh or thawed
frozen strawberries, blended)
1 Tbsp xylitol
1 tsp vanilla extract

GRANADILLA MOUSSE
1 cup fresh cream
Pulp from 2 granadillas
1 Tbsp xylitol
1 tsp vanilla extract

CARAMEL MOUSSE
1 cup fresh cream
4 Tbsp cold Quick Caramel Syrup
(p. 180)
1 tsp vanilla extract (plus a sugar-
free choc-mint block to transform
it into peppermint crisp mousse)

LEMON CHEESECAKE MOUSSE
1 cup fresh cream
2 Tbsp cream cheese
2 Tbsp lemon juice
1 Tbsp xylitol
1 tsp vanilla extract

Whip all the ingredients together using an electric mixer until fluffy and decadent.

Yields 3 servings.
Chocolate mousse: 4 g carbs per serving.
Berry mousse: 6 g carbs per serving.
Granadilla mousse: 5 g carbs per serving.
Caramel mousse: 6 g carbs per serving.
Lemon cheesecake mousse: 4 g carbs per serving.

LEKKER TIPS

- These can all be enjoyed as a dessert on their own or can be added as toppings or fillings for cakes, waffles, scones or brownies.

Caramel pecan topping

4 Tbsp butter
1 Tbsp xylitol
2 Tbsp fresh cream
4 Tbsp roughly chopped
pecan nuts

Melt the butter in a small saucepan on medium–high heat. Add the xylitol and stir until it has dissolved. Add the cream and allow to bubble and thicken for 1 minute. Lastly, add the chopped pecans, turn the heat to low and allow to thicken and brown for 1 minute. Remove from heat and allow to cool.

This goes particularly well with Vanilla Ice Cream (p. 165), but can also be used on home-made cheese balls, or as a topping for Pancakes (p. 160), waffles, cakes or brownies.

Yields 6 servings at 5.8 g carbs per serving.

Frozen 'yoghurt'

THESE ARE GREAT FOR HOT DAYS, SNACKS OR LUNCHBOXES. FOR THE LATTER, JUST FREEZE IN A SMALL PLASTIC CONTAINER WITH A LID AND BY FIRST BREAK IT WILL BE A NICE SCOOPABLE CONSISTENCY. ENJOY AS A SMOOTHIE FRESH OUT OF THE BLENDER OR FREEZE THEM IN POPSICLE MOULDS.

1 cup frozen berries of choice
1 cup fresh cream
1 cup amasi
1 Tbsp xylitol
1 tsp vanilla extract

Blend all the ingredients together using a stick blender and eat right away or portion into little cups and freeze.

Yields 6 servings at 5 g carbs per serving.

Quick ice cream for an ice-cream maker

VANILLA ICE CREAM
2 cups fresh cream
1 cup full-cream milk
½ tsp stevia powder
1 tsp xylitol
2 tsp quality vanilla extract

CHOCOLATE ICE CREAM
2 cups fresh cream
1 cup full-cream milk
½ tsp stevia powder
1 tsp xylitol
1 slightly heaped Tbsp cocoa powder
2 tsp vanilla extract

FRESH AND ZESTY LEMON ICE CREAM
2 cups fresh cream
1 cup full-cream milk
½ tsp stevia powder
1 tsp xylitol
Juice of 2 Lemons
Grated zest of 1 lemon
2 tsp vanilla extract

Mix all the ingredients using a stick blender and then transfer to the ice-cream maker. Churn for 15–20 minutes.

Each variation yields 6 servings at 5 g carbs per serving.

Cakes, Cookies and Treats

Granadilla and lime cake

CAKE

⅓ cup butter, at room temperature
4 Tbsp xylitol
2 free-range eggs
⅓ cup fresh cream
⅓ cup full-cream milk
1 tsp vanilla extract
1 Tbsp lime juice
Pulp of 1 granadilla
⅔ cup flax meal
⅔ cup fine desiccated coconut
1 cup almond or macadamia flour
1 Tbsp baking powder

CREAM CHEESE ICING

3 Tbsp butter, at room temperature
½ cup cream cheese, at room temperature
Grated zest and juice of ½ lime
2 Tbsp xylitol (ground in a coffee grinder)
⅓ cup fresh cream, stiffly whipped
½ cup coconut flakes

Preheat the oven to 180 °C.

For the cake, use an electric mixer and cream the butter and xylitol together. Add the eggs, cream, milk, vanilla, lime juice and granadilla pulp and mix well.

Place all the dry ingredients into a mixing bowl. Add the wet mixture to the dry mixture and mix well. Pour the batter into a buttered 23-cm-diameter cake pan and bake for 30–35 minutes or until the cake is spongy, firm and brown. Usually the cake will start to pull away from the sides of the pan when ready, but insert a knife to make sure. Allow to cool in the pan before turning out and icing.

For the icing, use an electric mixer to cream the butter, cream cheese, lime zest and juice, and xylitol until fluffy. Fold in the whipped cream. Toast the coconut flakes in a dry pan.

Spread the icing over the cooled cake and then sprinkle over the toasted coconut flakes.

Yields 8 servings at about 8 g carbs per serving.

Chocolate crème de la crème cake

IF YOU WANT TO MAKE A SINGLE LAYER CAKE, USE HALF THE INGREDIENTS FOR THE BATTER.

CAKE
2 cups nut flour (or pumpkin seed meal)
1 cup fine desiccated coconut
2 Tbsp baking powder
6 Tbsp cocoa powder
1 cup butter, at room temperature
6 Tbsp xylitol
2 tsp vanilla extract
1 cup full-cream milk
6 free-range eggs

MOUSSE FILLING
1 cup fresh cream
2 Tbsp cocoa powder
½ Tbsp xylitol

CHOCOLATE GANACHE
1 cup fresh cream
3–4 Tbsp cocoa powder
2 Tbsp butter
1 Tbsp xylitol
Handful macadamia nuts (optional)

Preheat the oven to 180 °C.

For the cake, mix the flour, coconut, baking powder and cocoa powder together in a mixing bowl.

In a separate bowl, cream the butter and xylitol together. Add the vanilla, milk and eggs and mix well. Add the wet ingredients to the dry ingredients and mix well. Divide the batter evenly between 2 x 23-cm-diameter cake pans.

Bake for 15–20 minutes until the cake is spongy and set. Test with a knife. Turn out the cakes onto a wire rack to cool completely.

For the mousse filling, whisk all the ingredients together until it resembles whipped cream. Once the cakes have cooled, sandwich them together with the mousse.

For the topping, place the cream, cocoa powder, butter and xylitol in a small saucepan on medium heat and stir until it has a thicker, glossy consistency. Remove from heat and stir in the nuts. Leave to cool for a minute and then pour over the top layer of the cake.

Yields 12 servings at 10 g carbs per serving.

Chocolate, butterscotch and berry cake

½ quantity Chocolate Crème de la Crème Cake batter (above)

BUTTERSCOTCH SAUCE
4 Tbsp butter
3 Tbsp xylitol
4 Tbsp fresh cream

TOPPINGS
¾ cup fresh cream, whipped
12 fresh or frozen berries

Bake a single layer cake as per the recipe.

For the sauce, melt the butter in a saucepan on medium to high heat and add the xylitol. Once the xylitol has dissolved, add the cream and allow to bubble, but keep stirring so that it does not boil over. Turn the heat down a bit and simmer until it has a darker, thick and glossy consistency. Allow the sauce to cool for a few minutes before pouring it over the cake. Allow the sauce to cool completely on the cake and then top with the whipped cream and lovely bright berries.

Yields 10 medium slices at about 7 g carbs per slice.

Chocolate crème de la crème cake

Lamingtons

Lamingtons

CAKE
1 x Basic Vanilla Sponge Cake
batter (p. 172)
1½ cups fine desiccated coconut

SYRUP
4 Tbsp xylitol
½ tsp cream of tartar
2 Tbsp cocoa powder
¾ cup boiling water
1 Tbsp butter
1 tsp vanilla extract

For the cake, make the batter and pour it into a wax paper-lined rectangular, deep sheet pan or a brownie pan. Silicone pans work well too. Bake for 18–25 minutes. Turn out onto a wire rack and allow to cool, then cut into equal-size cubes.

For the syrup, mix the xylitol, cream of tartar, cocoa and boiling water together in a saucepan. Place on medium to high heat, stirring continuously. Boil for 2 minutes. Add the butter and vanilla and then turn down the heat until it is just enough to keep the syrup warm.

Dip the cake cubes into the syrup, place on a wire rack and allow the excess to drip off for a few minutes. Roll the cubes in the coconut.

Yields 24 squares at 3.4 g carbs per square.

Orange zest cake

CAKE
½ quantity Basic Vanilla Sponge
Cake batter (p. 172)
Grated zest of 1 orange
1 Tbsp orange juice

ORANGE SYRUP
2 Tbsp butter
4 Tbsp fresh cream
4 Tbsp orange juice
Grated orange zest
1 Tbsp xylitol

For the cake, make the batter and add the grated orange zest and orange juice. Pour into a wax paper-lined loaf pan or a silicone pan. Bake for 18–24 minutes or until the batter is firm and browned – do a knife test to be sure. Turn out onto a wire rack and allow to cool.

For the syrup, place all the ingredients in a saucepan on high heat and allow to bubble and reduce for a minute or two. Stir with a whisk to make sure the sauce does not burn. Remove from heat.

Drizzle the orange syrup over the cake and let it soak in. Serve with a dollop of whipped cream on the side.

Yields 10 medium slices at 3.4 g carbs per slice.

Basic vanilla sponge cake

THIS ONE RECIPE CAN TRANSFORM INTO MULTIPLE FAMILY FAVOURITES.

SPONGE CAKE BATTER
½ cup butter, at room temperature
6 Tbsp xylitol
4 free-range eggs
¾ cup full-cream milk or amasi
2 tsp vanilla extract
2½ cups almond flour
Pinch salt
1 Tbsp baking powder
½ cup coconut meal

Preheat the oven to 180 °C.

Cream the butter and xylitol together in a mixing bowl. Whisk in the eggs. Slowly add the milk and vanilla and whisk until creamy.

Sift the almond flour, salt and baking powder into a separate mixing bowl. Add the coconut meal. Add the wet ingredients to the dry ingredients and mix well.

This makes a very runny batter.

Butter a 23-cm-diameter cake pan, a deep rectangular brownie pan or 2 loaf pans. Line the pans with wax paper or use silicone pans.

Bake for 20–30 minutes, depending on the pans you use and how thick the layer of batter is. The cake is ready when lightly browned, spongy and firm. Do a knife test to double-check. Allow to cool in the pan and then turn out.

Now you can use the sponge cake to build a layer cake or sculpt a birthday cake of your choice. You can decorate using the icings given below.

Yields 16 servings at 4 g carbs per serving.

Basic vanilla icing

3 Tbsp xylitol
2 Tbsp butter, at room temperature
1 tsp vanilla extract
½ cup cream cheese, at room temperature
4 Tbsp fresh cream

Grind the xylitol for a few seconds in a coffee grinder to yield a superfine powdered 'sugar'. Using an electric mixer, cream the xylitol, butter and vanilla together. Add the cream cheese and cream and mix to a smooth icing. Add a tiny bit of milk if you need to make it a bit more pliable.

Add flavours such as 2 Tbsp lemon juice, 1 tsp coffee dissolved in 1 Tbsp water, 3 Tbsp strawberry purée or 2 Tbsp granadilla pulp to the base icing.

One batch of icing adds about 1 g carbs for each serving of cake or 0.5 g carbs per cupcake.

Basic chocolate icing

3 Tbsp xylitol
2 Tbsp butter, at room temperature
2 tsp vanilla extract
½ cup cream cheese, at room temperature
6 Tbsp fresh cream
3 Tbsp cocoa powder

Grind the xylitol for a few seconds in a coffee grinder to yield a super-fine powdered 'sugar'. Using an electric mixer, cream the xylitol, butter and vanilla together. Add the cream cheese, cream and cocoa and mix to make a rich chocolate icing. Add a tiny bit of milk if you need to make it a bit more pliable.

One batch of icing adds about 1.2 g carbs for each serving of cake or 0.75 g carbs per cupcake.

Cupcakes

Pour 1 quantity Basic Vanilla Sponge Cake batter (p. 172) into 24 lined cupcake holes. Bake for 10–12 minutes. Cool completely before icing.

Yields 24 cupcakes at 2.8 g carbs per cupcake.

Cheesecake with berry coulis

CRUST

1½ cups nut meal (pecan, walnut, almond or macadamia)

4 Tbsp melted butter

1 Tbsp xylitol

1 Tbsp cocoa powder (optional)

2 tsp psyllium husk powder

3 Tbsp boiling water

CHEESECAKE FILLING

1 x 230 g block cream cheese

4 large free-range eggs

1 cup sour cream (or fresh cream with a squeeze lemon juice added)

1 Tbsp vanilla extract

4 Tbsp xylitol

BERRY COULIS

1 cup mixed frozen berries

2 Tbsp water

1 Tbsp butter

1 Tbsp xylitol

½ tsp psyllium husk powder (as thickener)

Preheat the oven to 200 °C.

For the crust, mix all the ingredients together and press into a 1-cm-thick layer on the base of 4 single-serving ramekins, 10 cupcake liners or 1 medium, loose-bottomed, round cake pan.

For the filling, use an electric mixer or food processor to fluff the cream cheese slightly. Add the eggs, one at a time, mixing well after each addition. Add the sour cream, vanilla and xylitol. Don't overwork the mixture. Pour the filling over the crust in your preferred dish.

Bake for 15–20 minutes, then lower the oven temperature to 180 °C and continue baking for another 20–30 minutes. The cheese-cake is ready when a crack appears in the batter. Allow to cool.

For the coulis, stir all the ingredients, except the husks, together in a saucepan on medium to high heat. Reduce heat after all the berries are thawed and have boiled for at least 3 minutes. Allow the sauce to simmer and reduce for 6–7 minutes, stirring often but gently. Try to keep the berries as whole as possible.

Stir in the psyllium husks and mix well into the sauce. Remove from heat and allow to cool before scooping over the cheesecake just before serving.

Yields 6–8 servings at 8 g carbs per serving.

Carrot cake

ON A LOW-CARB LIFESTYLE, WE GENERALLY LIMIT THE USE OF UNDERGROUND VEGGIES DUE TO THEIR
HIGHER CARB CONTENT. THIS RECIPE HAS BEEN ADAPTED SO THAT A LITTLE BIT GOES A LONG WAY,
BUT YOU WILL STILL HAVE THE CARROT TASTE WITHOUT ALL THE CARBS.

CAKE

2 Tbsp butter, at room
temperature
5 Tbsp xylitol
4 free-range eggs
½ cup butter, melted
1½ cups nut meal (almond or
pecan)
¾ cup coconut meal
2 tsp baking powder
1 tsp ground cinnamon
1 tsp ground ginger
¼ tsp bicarbonate of soda
½ cup roughly chopped pecan nuts
½ cup grated carrots
1 cup grated pumpkin
1 cup grated yellow patty pans

ICING

7 Tbsp butter, at room
temperature
½ x 230 g block cream cheese
2 tsp lemon juice
2 Tbsp xylitol

Preheat the oven to 180 °C.

For the cakes, use an electric mixer to cream the room temperature butter and xylitol together. Add the eggs and melted butter and
mix well.

In a separate bowl, mix the nut meal, coconut meal, baking powder, cinnamon, ginger, bicarbonate of soda and pecans together.
Pour in the egg mixture and add the grated veggies, then fold into
the dry ingredients.

Divide the batter between 2 buttered loaf pans and bake for
30 minutes or until the cakes are fairly browned and firm to the
touch. Allow to cool in the pan and then turn out.

For the icing, use an electric mixer to blend all the ingredients
together until smooth. Spread over the carrot cakes.

Yields 16 medium slices at 5 g carbs per slice.

Chocolate brownies

Lemon poppy cake

CAKE
⅓ cup melted butter
5 Tbsp xylitol
3 free-range eggs
6 Tbsp full-cream milk
1 tsp vanilla extract
6 Tbsp lemon juice
2–3 Tbsp poppy seeds, plus extra to decorate
1½ cups almond meal or flour
2 tsp baking powder
½ tsp bicarbonate of soda

ICING
½ x 230 g block cream cheese
4 Tbsp butter
1 Tbsp xylitol
3 Tbsp lemon juice

Preheat the oven to 180 °C.

For the cake, blend the melted butter, xylitol, eggs, milk, vanilla, lemon juice and poppy seeds together in a mixing bowl.

In a separate bowl, mix the almond meal, baking powder and bicarbonate of soda together. Add the wet ingredients to the dry ingredients and stir well.

Pour the runny batter into a silicone ring mould or a regular round pan lined with wax paper. Bake for 20–35 minutes (depending on the type of pan) until brown and firm. It's okay for the cake to look slightly folded on top.

Allow to cool in the pan and then turn out.

For the icing, use an electric mixer to mix all the ingredients together until light and fluffy. Spread the icing over the case and sprinkle with extra poppy seeds.

Yields 8 servings at 8 g per serving.

Chocolate brownies

1 cup nut meal or flour (almond or pecan)
½ cup cocoa powder
1 tsp baking powder
½ tsp bicarbonate of soda
3 Tbsp xylitol
2 free-range eggs
7 Tbsp fresh cream
4 Tbsp melted butter

Preheat the oven to 180 °C.

Mix all the dry ingredients together in a mixing bowl. In a separate bowl, whisk all the wet ingredients together. Add the wet ingredients to the dry ingredients and mix well. Pour the batter into a square brownie pan or a silicone muffin tray. Bake for 8–10 minutes until cracks appear on the surface. If you like a moist, 'gooey' brownie, 8 minutes is fine. For a fluffy brownie, bake for 10–12 minutes.

Serve with Chocolate, Berry or Caramel Mousse (p. 163), Quick Ice Cream (p. 165), Chocolate Ganache (p. 168) or any icing from this chapter.

Yields 8–10 brownies at 4 g carbs per brownie.

Waffle option

This recipe makes a lovely waffle too for a waffle machine. Separate the eggs: add the yolks when you mix the wet ingredients, and then fold in the stiffly beaten egg whites after the batter is mixed.

Midnight snack in a mug

THIS IS MY TAKE ON A CHOCOLATE PUDDING WITH IT'S OWN SAUCE. I MUST SAY,
IN UNDER 5 MINUTES THIS ONE REALLY HITS THE SPOT!

2 Tbsp coconut meal
1 Tbsp cocoa powder
1 Tbsp xylitol
1 tsp baking powder
1 large free-range egg
1 Tbsp amasi, full-cream milk or
fresh cream
2 Tbsp melted coconut oil

SAUCE
3 Tbsp hot water
1 Tbsp cocoa powder

Spoon the coconut meal, cocoa powder, xylitol and baking powder into a mug. Add the egg, amasi and coconut oil and stir well.

For the sauce, mix the water and cocoa powder together and pour it over the back of a spoon onto the batter in the mug.

Microwave for about 90 seconds on high until the cake is spongy and the sauce has sunk to the bottom of the mug.

Yields 1 serving at 7 g carbs.

Cheat's 10-minute chocolate cake

CAKE
1 cup almond meal or pumpkin
seed meal
4 Tbsp fine desiccated coconut
2 tsp baking powder
2 Tbsp cocoa powder
2 Tbsp xylitol
Pinch salt
2 Tbsp melted butter
2 free-range eggs
½ cup amasi or full-cream milk

QUICK CARAMEL SYRUP
2 Tbsp butter
1½ Tbsp xylitol
½ cup fresh cream
1 tsp vanilla exstract

For the cake, mix all the dry ingredients in a microwave-safe mixing bowl. Add the wet ingredients and stir well using a fork. Cook in the microwave on high for 5–6 minutes. Check progress at around 4 minutes. The cake is ready when it is spongy, firm and pulls away from the sides of the bowl (you want this cake to be moist rather than dry).

For the caramel syrup, melt the butter in a small saucepan on medium to high heat. Add the xylitol and stir until it has dissolved completely. Add the cream and stir for 1 minute. Allow the sauce to boil, forming big bubbles, then adjust the heat to medium and allow the sauce to simmer gently and reduce for 2–3 minutes. The sauce will turn a lovely caramel colour.

Tip the cake onto a serving plate and pour over the syrup. Enjoy!

The cake yields 6–8 servings at 8 carbs per serving.
The sauce yields about ²/₃ cup at 8 g carbs altogether.

LEKKER TIPS

- The Quick Caramel Syrup is an ideal topping for ice cream, cake and waffles. It's slightly runny texture makes it easy to pour and enjoy.
- The syrup can be stored in a jar in the refrigerator. Reheat slightly before use.

Cheat's 10-minute chocolate cake

Blackberry poppers

1 cup nut meal
½ cup coconut flakes
1 tsp baking powder
½ tsp bicarbonate of soda
2 Tbsp xylitol
1 Tbsp psyllium husks
1 free-range egg
2 Tbsp melted coconut oil
About 1 cup frozen blackberries

Preheat the oven to 180 °C.

Mix all the dry ingredients together in a mixing bowl. Add the egg and coconut oil and mix through. Roll the dough into balls the size of a big marble and space apart on a baking tray. Press a frozen berry firmly into the centre of each cookie ball. Bake for 10–12 minutes until the berries ooze juice and the cookies are brown and firm.

Yields about 18 cookies at less than 2 g carbs per cookie.

Rusks

2 cups nut meal or flour
1 cup fine desiccated coconut
½ cup medium desiccated coconut
1 cup seed mix (flaxseed, sesame, pumpkin, sunflower)
½ cup extra sunflower seeds
1 cup ground seed mix (grind in a coffee grinder)
4 tsp baking powder
4 Tbsp psyllium husk fibre
8 Tbsp xylitol
1¼ cups butter, at room temperature
4 free-range eggs
2 cups amasi or buttermilk

Preheat the oven to 180 °C.

Mix the nut meal, coconut, seeds, ground seed mix, baking powder and psyllium together in a mixing bowl.

In a separate bowl, cream the xylitol and butter together using an electric mixer. Add the eggs and buttermilk. Stir the liquid mixture into the dry ingredients and mix well.

Divide the batter evenly between 2 rectangular brownie pans. If you bake the rusks in a thinner layer they dry out better and crumb less. Bake for 35–40 minutes until brown and set. If you use a fan-assisted oven, this could take less time.

Allow to cool in the pan for 10 minutes and then cut into your preferred portion sizes while still in the pan. Gently take out with a spatula and arrange on an oven rack. Dry out for a few hours in a very low oven or eat like a hot scone!

Yields 70–80 rusks, depending on your portion size of preference, at 1.5–2 g carbs per rusk.

NOTE: Because of the high oil content in nut and seed flours and meals, these rusks take a bit longer to dry than the traditional version. I do mine in intervals, drying them for 2–3 hours and then allowing them to cool first before drying them again for another hour or two. The oil in the meal can also burn easily when drying, so it is important to have your oven set really low. I roll up a dish towel and wedge it in between the oven and the oven door. Lastly, again because of the oil content in the nut flour, these rusks don't harden as much as conventional rusks, but they are 'dip-able' and taste like the real McCoy!

Sweet scones

2 cups almond flour
½ cup fine desiccated coconut
1 Tbsp baking powder
1 Tbsp xylitol
Pinch salt
6 Tbsp cold butter
2 free-range eggs
⅓ cup full-cream milk or amasi,
plus extra for brushing

Preheat the oven to 180 °C. Place the almond flour, coconut, baking powder, xylitol and salt into a mixing bowl. Rub in the butter until the mixture resembles breadcrumbs. Whisk the eggs and milk together and then mix into the dry ingredients. Without overworking the dough, scoop heaped tablespoons of dough onto a buttered baking tray and brush with milk (or egg wash if you prefer). Bake for 15–20 minutes until brown and set (test with a knife). Serve with fresh strawberries and cream or Berry Jam (p. 136).

Yields 8 large scones at 4.5 g carbs per scone or 12 medium rustic scones at 3 g carbs per scone.

LEKKER TIPS

- For daintier scones, scoop spoonfuls of dough into a 12-hole cupcake pan.

Choc-Coconut creams

Choc-Coconut creams

COOKIES
¾ cup fine desiccated coconut
1½ cups medium desiccated coconut
¾ cup almond flour
2 Tbsp cocoa powder
1 tsp baking powder
7 Tbsp butter, at room temperature
4 Tbsp xylitol
1 egg
½ cup boiling water

FILLING
½ cup fresh cream
2 Tbsp cocoa powder
1 Tbsp xylitol
2 tsp psyllium husk powder

Preheat the oven to 180 °C.

For the cookies, mix the coconut, almond flour, cocoa powder and baking powder together in a mixing bowl.

In a separate bowl, mix the butter and xylitol together until creamy. Add the egg.

Add the egg mixture to the dry ingredients, add the boiling water and mix well. Roll the dough into giant lollipop-sized balls. Arrange on a buttered baking tray, press down slightly with two fingers and bake for about 20 minutes until golden brown. Cool on a wire rack.

For the filling, combine all the ingredients in a saucepan on medium heat and stir until it reaches a thick custard-like consistency. Cool for a minute before sandwiching the cookies together with the filling. Store in an airtight container.

Yields about 18 double cookies at 2.5 g carbs per cookie.

Ginger cookies

½ cup butter, at room temperature
5 Tbsp xylitol
1 egg
4 Tbsp fine desiccated coconut
¾ cup nut meal or flour
1½ cups pumpkin seed meal
2 Tbsp psyllium husk fibre
2 tsp ground ginger
2 tsp ground cinnamon
1 tsp bicarbonate of soda
4 Tbsp hot water

Preheat the oven to 180 °C.

Whisk the butter until fluffy, then add the xylitol and mix until it has a fluffy, creamy consistency. Add the egg and mix well.

Mix all the dry ingredients together and then add to the egg mixture. Lastly, stir in the water, mix and refrigerate for 10 minutes.

Roll the batter into jawbreaker-size balls, place on a buttered baking tray and press down with a fork. Bake for 12–15 minutes until brown and hardened. Once all your cookies are done baking, put them back in the switched-off oven and leave to cool completely. Store in an airtight container.

Yields about 40 cookies at about 1 g carb per cookie.

IMPORTANT: An LCHF lifestyle means baking with nuts and seeds, and our 'flour' has a high oil base that WILL change baking the way you've known it up until now. This ginger cookie is absolutely delicious, but it has neither the hardness nor the 1½ cups of sugar and golden syrup like the original recipe. It is still 'dip-able' and filled with magnesium, fibre and good fats, which makes for a non sugar-spiking, brain boosting, decarbed treat!

Chewy choc chippers

1 cup pumpkin seed meal or almond flour
3 Tbsp fine desiccated coconut
2 Tbsp cocoa powder
2 tsp baking powder
3 Tbsp xylitol
6 Tbsp butter, at room temperature
1 free-range egg
1 tsp vanilla extract
6 Tbsp full-cream milk

Preheat the oven to 180 °C.

Place the pumpkin seed meal, coconut, cocoa powder and baking powder in a mixing bowl.

In a separate bowl, whisk the xylitol and butter together until creamy. Whisk in the egg, vanilla and milk. Add the wet mixture to the dry mixture.

Scoop tablespoonsful of batter onto a wax paper-lined baking tray with enough space to allow the cookies to spread out. Bake for 8 minutes.

Yields 12–15 cookies at 2.5 g carbs per cookie.

- Make minty choc chippers by sprinkling 3 chopped Caring Candies™ Humbugs (available at most large retail supermarkets) and 3 chopped blocks Caring Candies™ Sugar-Free Milk Chocolate or 3 chopped blocks 85% cocoa dark chocolate onto the hot cookies, straight from the oven.

Fruity coco-nilla cookies

COOKIES
6 Tbsp butter, at room temperature
3 Tbsp xylitol
1 free-range egg
6 Tbsp full-cream milk
1 tsp vanilla extract
1½ cups almond meal or flour
8 Tbsp desiccated coconut
2 tsp baking powder

LEMON DROP ICING
2 Tbsp each cream cheese and butter, at room temperature
2 Tbsp xylitol
1 Tbsp lemon juice
1 Tbsp fresh cream

Preheat the oven to 180 °C.

For the cookies, whisk the butter and xylitol until creamy. Add the egg, milk and vanilla and whisk until fluffy.

Mix all the dry ingredients together in a bowl. Add the egg mixture and mix well. Scoop slightly heaped tablespoonsful of batter onto a buttered, wax paper-lined baking tray. Leave enough room for the cookies to spread. Bake for 10–12 minutes or until firm and brown. Allow to cool on the tray and then peel off the wax paper.

For the icing, whisk all the ingredients together until glossy and thick. Scoop onto the cookies. Top with crushed sugar-free candies (just remember, 3 pieces of candy counts as a serving for a day).

Yields 18 cookies at 2.7 g carbs per cookie.

- For vanilla choc-chip cookies, use the above recipe and add 3 chopped blocks of a Caring Candies™ chocolate bar or 85% cocoa dark chocolate to the dry ingredients before adding the egg mixture.

Fruity coco-nilla cookies

Marshmallows

Marshmallows

½ cup xylitol or ½ tsp debittered stevia powder
⅔ cup warm water
4 Tbsp gelatine
½ cup cold water
2 Tbsp rose-water or vanilla essence
1 drop food colouring (if you can get a hold of natural food colour from your health shop, even better) (optional)
6 Tbsp fine desiccated coconut

Place the xylitol and warm water in a small saucepan on medium heat and stir until the xylitol dissolves completely.

Add the gelatine to the cold water, let it 'sponge' for a few minutes and then stir it into the xylitol syrup. Boil the mixture for 4–5 minutes, stirring frequently. Remove from heat and cool to room temperature.

Transfer the mixture to a large mixing bowl and use an electric mixer until almost doubled in volume. Add the flavouring and colour and whisk for another 8–10 minutes or until soft peaks form.

Pour the mixture into a lined rusk pan or a square or rectangular glass dish. Allow to set for 1 hour.

Cut into squares with a knife dipped in hot water. Cover with coconut and store in an airtight container.

Yields 16 squares at 1.75 g carbs per square.

LEKKER TIPS

- You can experiment with flavour combinations to your heart's content.
- These make awesome hot cocoa toppings too.

Brain booster bars

COCONUT IS A WONDERFUL ENERGY BOOSTER WITH THE ABILITY TO KEEP BLOOD SUGAR SPIKES AT BAY. ALMONDS ARE HIGH IN HEALTHY FATS AND CONTAIN RIBOFLAVIN, L-CARNITINE AND NUTRIENTS THAT BOOST BRAIN ACTIVITY. AS A BONUS, THE FIBRE CONTENT IN THESE BARS PROMOTES HEALTHY GUT FLORA AND DIGESTIVE HEALTH.
THE COCOA JUST ALLOWS US TO FEEL HAPPY AND RELAXED.

2 free-range eggs
½ cup melted butter
1½ cups nut meal or flour (almond or pecan)
1 cup fine desiccated coconut
1 cup coconut flakes
2 Tbsp cocoa powder
2 tsp baking powder
3 Tbsp xylitol
1 handful macadamia nuts
1 Caring Candies™ sugar-free chocolate bar, chopped

Preheat the oven to 180 °C.

Whisk the eggs and butter together. Add the rest of the ingredients and mix in to form a chunky batter. Pour into a buttered brownie tin. (I prefer a thicker bar and only spread it over half of my tin.) Bake for 15–20 minutes.

Make any basic icing from this chapter and spread over the top. Cut into cubes.

Yields 15 squares at 4 g carbs per square.

No-bake chocolate rum balls

THESE ARE GREAT WITH COFFEE, AS A ROMANTIC FIRESIDE SNACK, A LUNCHBOX TREAT OR EVEN A GIFT
FOR A FRIEND TAKING THE FIRST STEPS INTO A LOW-CARB LIFESTYLE.

2 Tbsp butter
4 Tbsp cream cheese
½ cup pumpkin seed meal
½ cup nut meal or flour
½ cup fine desiccated coconut
3 Tbsp cocoa powder
2 Tbsp xylitol
1–2 Tbsp dark rum or 1 tsp rum
essence, or even 1 tsp vanilla
extract for plain chocolate balls
Extra 4 Tbsp cocoa powder or
desiccated coconut for coating

Melt the butter and cream cheese in a small saucepan on medium heat. Add the pumpkin seed meal, nut meal, coconut, cocoa powder and xylitol while stirring so that the mixture forms a ball of dough. Add the rum. Remove from heat and place in a clean container or on a cutting board. Roll into large grape-size balls.

Roll the balls in the extra cocoa powder or desiccated coconut until completely covered.

Yields 16 balls at 1.6 g carbs per ball.

No-bake caramel cream cheese balls

2 Tbsp butter
3 Tbsp xylitol
4 Tbsp cream cheese
1 cup nut meal or flour
½ cup fine desiccated coconut
1 tsp vanilla extract
Extra 4 Tbsp fine desiccated
coconut for coating

Melt the butter, xylitol and cream cheese together in a saucepan on medium heat. Allow to simmer for 2 minutes to form a caramel-like sauce. Add the nut meal and coconut and stir until it forms a ball. Add the vanilla. Remove from heat and place in a clean container or on a cutting board. Roll into large grape-size balls.

Roll the balls in the extra coconut until completely covered.

Yields 16 balls at 1.5 g carbs per ball.

LEKKER TIPS

- **For lemon-flavoured balls:** Add 1 Tbsp lemon juice and the grated zest of ½ lemon to the batter.
- **For mocha balls:** Add 1 tsp good coffee powder dissolved in 1 Tbsp water to the batter.
- **For fruity-flavoured balls:** Add 1 Tbsp orange juice and the grated zest of ½ orange, or the pulp of 1 granadilla, or the pulp of 4–5 berries to the batter.

*No-bake caramel
cream cheese balls*

Beverages

Lemon simple syrup

ON A LOW-CARB DIET FRUIT SHOULD BE SEEN AS NATURE'S CANDIES AND THEREFORE USED SPARINGLY, SO I TRY TO INCORPO-RATE IT IN RECIPES WHERE IT CAN BE SPREAD OVER MANY PORTIONS. ALTHOUGH THIS SEEMS LIKE A LOT OF LEMON JUICE, THIS SYRUP WILL MAKE THREE LITRES OF LEMONADE ONCE DILUTED. THE COMBINATION OF XYLITOL AND STEVIA TAKES THE EDGE OFF THE STEVIA TASTE, BUT YOU CAN OMIT THE XYLITOL ALTOGETHER IF THE STEVIA DOES NOT BOTHER YOU ON ITS OWN.

2 cups water
¾ cup fresh lemon juice
¼ cup xylitol (optional)
1 tsp debittered stevia powder (or
add a bit more to taste)

Heat all the ingredients together in a saucepan on medium to high heat. Let it simmer for a few minutes, and then remove from heat and allow to cool. Store in a covered glass jar in the refrigerator.

Add 1 cup syrup to 4 cups sparkling or still water. Garnish with a slice of lemon and serve with ice.

Yields 15 x 200 ml cups at 1.6 g carbs per cup.

Lemon and lavender simple syrup

NB: Avoid lavender if you are pregnant.
Simply add 1 heaped Tbsp of fresh whole English lavender flowers to the hot Lemon Simple Syrup and allow to infuse for a few minutes. Strain and serve as above.

Yields 15 x 200 ml cups at 1.6 g carbs per cup.

Pink simple syrup

Purée 1 cup whole fresh or frozen and thawed strawberries in ½ cup water and add to the simmering Lemon Simple Syrup. Continue simmering while skimming off the excess foam for 3–4 minutes. Add 1 cup Pink Simple Syrup to 4 cups still or sparkling water and serve over ice with a slice of lemon and a frozen strawberry.

Yields 17 x 200 ml cups at around 2 g carbs per cup.

Granadilla simple syrup

Add the pulp of 2 granadillas to the simmering Lemon Simple Syrup. Continue simmering while skimming off the excess foam for 3–4 minutes. Add 1 cup Granadilla Simple Syrup to 4 cups still or sparkling water and serve with a slice of lemon and ice.

Yields 15 x 200 ml cups at almost 2 g carbs per cup.

LEKKER TIPS

- These simple syrups can be drizzled over vanilla cake or cupcakes and dusted with xylitol that's been powdered in a coffee grinder.
- Use as a base syrup for cocktails.
- All these syrups keep well in the refrigerator for at least 10 days.

Peach and apricot iced coconut tea

8 Freshpak® Junior Rooibos tea
bags, Peach & Apricot Flavour
2 cups boiling water
½ x 400 ml can coconut milk
1 cinnamon stick
1 Tbsp xylitol
Stevia liquid or powder to taste
1¼ cups ice-cold water
Crushed ice to serve

Allow the tea to steep in the boiling water for 5 minutes.

Remove the tea bags and add the coconut milk, cinnamon stick, xylitol and stevia to taste. Stir to dissolve while the tea mixture is still lukewarm.

Lastly, add the water and refrigerate until properly chilled. Serve over crushed ice.

Yields 5 x 200 ml cups of creamy iced tea at 2.8 g carbs per cup.

Vanilla berry iced tea

8 Freshpak® Junior Rooibos tea
bags, Strawberry & Vanilla Flavour
2 cups boiling water
1 Tbsp xylitol (optional)
Stevia liquid or powder to taste
6 cups ice-cold water
Crushed ice to serve
10 frozen strawberries
Fresh mint leaves or rosemary
flowers to garnish

Allow the tea to steep in the boiling water for 5 minutes.

Remove the tea bags and add the xylitol and stevia to taste. Stir to dissolve while the tea mixture is still lukewarm.

Lastly, add the water and refrigerate until properly chilled. Serve over crushed ice with a frozen strawberry and mint leaves or rosemary flowers.

Yields 10 x 200 ml cups of iced tea at less than 1 g carbs per cup.

REMINDER: The combination of xylitol and stevia takes the edge off the stevia taste, but you can omit the xylitol altogether if the stevia does not bother you on its own. Because xylitol has some empty kilojoules and carbs, I combine the two to get the best taste balance without the carbs. Stevia liquid or debittered powder will work. One teaspoon of stevia powder has the equivalent sweetness level of 1 cup sugar.

LEKKER TIPS

- Make your own iced tea with your favourite tea blends and add complementary sprigs of herbs, citrus slices or frozen berries for that extra pizzazz!

Naturally flavoured still or sparkling water

Add to 4–8 cups still or sparkling water:

Blueberry and rosemary water
4 Tbsp frozen blueberries and 1 sprig fresh rosemary.

Minted cucumber water
8 slices cucumber and 1 sprig fresh mint.

Ginger and orange water
2 slices fresh ginger and 3 slices orange.

Citrus water
5–6 thinly sliced lemons or limes.

LEKKER TIPS

- This smoothie is both decadent and filling. It can be enjoyed as a meal on its own.
- This would make a great 'yoghurt' snack for a picky eater.
- The mixture can be frozen as popsicles.

Raspberry–Avo smoothie

¼ avocado
½ cup amasi or double-cream plain yoghurt
1 tsp vanilla extract
1 Tbsp xylitol (optional)
⅔ cup fresh or frozen raspberries
¾ cup fresh cream

Place all the ingredients into your blender and blend away! Serve immediately over crushed ice.

Yields 2 satisfying servings at 10 g carbs per serving.

Caribbean coffee smoothie

¾ cup coconut milk
½ cup amasi
2 tsp instant coffee granules
1 Tbsp xylitol (optional)
2 Tbsp ground almonds (made in your coffee grinder or store bought)

Place all the ingredients into your blender and blend away! Serve immediately over crushed ice.

Yields 2 satisfying servings at about 10 g carbs per serving.

LEKKER TIPS

- Allow to chill and set in the refrigerator for a lovely mocha mousse.
- The mixture can be frozen as popsicles.
- They keep well in the refrigerator for at least 10 days.

Blueberry cheesecake smoothie

⅔ cup frozen blueberries
½ cup amasi or plain double-cream yoghurt
2 Tbsp cream cheese, at room temperature
½ cup fresh cream
½ cup water
1 Tbsp xylitol
1 tsp psyllium husks

Place all the ingredients into your blender and blend away! Serve immediately over crushed ice.

Yields 2 satisfying servings at about 10 g carbs per serving.

LEKKER TIPS

- This is a high-octane fat shake that will fuel you well into your day. It is also wonderful for gut health and has a fibre bonus.
- The mixture can be frozen as popsicles.

Chocolate and mint smoothie

½ cup fresh cream
2 sprigs fresh mint
2 Tbsp butter
2 Tbsp cocoa powder
1 Tbsp xylitol
1 cup full-cream milk
1 egg

Heat the cream and mint together in a saucepan on medium heat and allow the mint to infuse the cream for 5–7 minutes. Discard the mint and add the butter, cocoa and xylitol. Turn up the heat and whisk while the sauce thickens. Remove from heat and cool slightly. Blend the chocolate sauce, milk and egg together. Serve immediately.

Yields 2 servings at 9 g carbs per serving.

Caramel and macadamia nut smoothie

2 Tbsp butter
1 Tbsp xylitol
½ cup fresh cream
1 tsp vanilla extract
2 Tbsp ground macadamia nuts
(milled in a coffee grinder)
1 cup full-cream milk
1 egg

Melt the butter in a saucepan on medium heat, add the xylitol and whisk until it has dissolved. Add the cream and keep on whisking. It needs to bubble for 2–3 minutes into a nice, light caramel syrup. Add the vanilla and remove from heat. Cool.

Place the caramel sauce, nuts, milk and egg into the blender and blend away. Serve immediately over crushed ice.

Yields 2 smaller servings of about 10 g carbs per serving.

Kidney tonic

BUCHU IS PART OF SOUTH AFRICA'S UNIQUE FLORAL KINGDOM. IT HAS AN EFFECTIVE FLUSHING ACTION ON THE KIDNEYS AND ALSO CONTAINS MANY DISEASE-PREVENTING FLAVANOIDS. BERRIES ARE AMONG THE TOP 15 SUPER FOODS, AND ARE STRONGLY RECOMMENDED FOR KIDNEY AND DIGESTIVE CARE.

2 buchu tea bags (available from
most retail and health stores)
1½ cups boiling water
½ cup frozen blackberries
½ cup frozen raspberries
A little xylitol or stevia (optional)

Let the buchu tea bags steep in the boiling water for 5 minutes.
Remove the tea bags and blend the buchu tea concentrate and frozen berries for a few seconds in your blender.

Yields 2 servings at 3.5 g carbs per serving.

Chocolate milk for kids

½ cup cold full-cream milk
½ cup fresh cream
1 Tbsp xylitol
1 tsp vanilla extract
½ tsp psyllium husks
1 tsp cocoa powder

Place all the ingredients in a blender and blend well. Or heat up and add a knob of butter for a divine hot choc!

Yields two kiddies' size servings at 6.5 g carbs per serving.

LEKKER TIPS

- Substitute the dairy with coconut milk or coconut cream for dairy intolerance, and add a raw egg to the cold mix for picky eaters. It will serve as a cell-building protein too!
- For a strawberry flavour, simply add 5–7 whole fresh or frozen strawberries instead of cocoa.

Chocolate milk for kids

Buttered rum

Hot cocoa

A PERFECT WINTER'S SNACK.

¾ cup coconut milk
¾ cup full-cream milk
1 Tbsp xylitol
2 Tbsp butter
2 slightly heaped Tbsp cocoa powder

Place all the ingredients in a saucepan on medium heat, whisking often. Simmer very gently for about 1 minute.

Yields 2 delightful, almost custardy hot chocs at 8 g carbs per serving.

LEKKER TIPS

- **Caribbean Hot Chocolate:** Follow the basic Hot Cocoa recipe and stir 1 tsp ground allspice or mixed spice into the mixture. Top with whipped cream and dust with ground cinnamon.
- **Mexican Hot Chocolate:** Follow the basic Hot Cocoa recipe and stir 1 tsp ground allspice or mixed spice into the mixture. Top with whipped cream and dust with a few chilli flakes as a warning!
- For dairy intolerance, use 400 ml coconut milk and omit the cow's milk.

Buttered rum

2 whole cloves
2 cardamom seeds
1 tsp mixed spice
1 cinnamon stick
1½ cups boiling water
2 pieces orange peel
1–2 tsp xylitol
1 Tbsp butter
4 tsp dark rum
1 Tbsp fresh cream (optional)
A sprinkle of nutmeg and a cinnamon stick to serve (optional)

Place the cloves, cardamom, mixed spice, cinnamon, water, orange peel, xylitol and butter in a saucepan on medium to high heat. Bring to a boil and infuse for about 3 minutes.
Remove from heat and strain into one big mug or 2 cups. Stir in the rum. If you want a bit more decadence, stir in the cream, pop in the cinnamon stick and sprinkle with nutmeg.

Yields 1 big mug or 2 teacups at less than 2 g carbs for the mug-sized serving.

Berry hot toddy

THIS BERRY TODDY WILL KNOCK YOUR SOCKS OFF! IT SIMPLY IS THE FRIENDLIEST, FRUITIEST, MOST COMFORTING, SOUL-HUGGING TODDY OF THEM ALL. (I AM NUTS ABOUT BERRIES, SO I MIGHT NOT BE 100 PER CENT NEUTRAL ON THIS STATEMENT.)

1½ cups boiling water
1 Freshpak® Junior Rooibos tea bag, Apple Flavour
⅓ cup mixed frozen berries
½ tsp ground cinnamon
2 cardamom seeds
1 Tbsp butter
1 piece orange peel
1–2 tsp xylitol
4 tsp spiced or dark rum
1 cinnamon stick

Place all the ingredients, except the rum and cinnamon stick, into a saucepan on medium heat and allow to simmer for 5 minutes.

Take out the tea bag and cardamom seeds. If you would like it smooth, use a stick blender to purée the berries. (I leave mine whole and eat the berries at the end for an experience that lingers longer...)

Stir in the rum with the cinnamon stick, pour into a mug and sip.

Yields 1 big mug or 2 teacups at 4.5 g carbs for the mug-sized serving.

Chai spiced hot toddy

THIS HOT TODDY IS ONE OF MY FAVOURITES. IT IS PROUDLY SOUTH AFRICAN TOO, AS I INCORPORATE THE NATURAL SWEET FLAVOUR OF ROOIBOS TEA. THE COCONUT MILK AND BUTTER INFUSED WITH SPICES THICKENS EVER SO SLIGHTLY TO A GOOD HOT-CHOCOLATE CONSISTENCY.

1 rooibos chai tea bag (available at most general retail stores)
½ cup boiling water
¼ x 400 ml can coconut milk
1 Tbsp butter
1 tsp mixed spice
1 tsp ground cinnamon
1 Tbsp xylitol
1 cinnamon stick
4 tsp spiced rum

Steep the tea bag in the boiling water for 2–3 minutes.

Remove the tea bag and place the tea and the rest of the ingredients, except the rum, into a saucepan on medium–high heat and allow to simmer for 3–4 minutes.

Remove from heat and stir in the rum. Strain into one big mug or 2 cups. Pop the cinnamon stick back into the mug and enjoy!

Yields 1 mug or 2 teacups at 6 g carbs for the mug-sized serving.

Berry hot toddy

Conversion Chart

Metric	US cups
5 ml	1 tsp
15 ml	1 Tbsp
60 ml	4 Tbsp or ¼ cup
80 ml	⅓ cup
125 ml	½ cup
160 ml	⅔ cup
200 ml	¾ cup
250 ml	1 cup

Index

Page numbers in **bold** indicate photographs.